Building Technology 1

Jack Bowyer

Dipl. Arch. (Leeds) - Architect

Illustrations prepared by

Peter Bowyer

Dipl. Arch. (Brighton)

NEWNES-BUTTERWORTHS
TEC
TECHNICIAN SERIES

THE BUTTERWORTH GROUP

UNITED KINGDOM
Butterworth & Co (Publishers) Ltd
London: 88 Kingsway, WC2B 6AB

AUSTRALIA
Butterworths Pty Ltd
Sydney: 586 Pacific Highway, NSW 2067
Also at Melbourne, Brisbane, Adelaide and Perth

CANADA
Butterworth & Co (Canada) Ltd
Toronto: 2265 Midland Avenue, Scarborough, Ontario, M1P 4S1

NEW ZEALAND
Butterworths of New Zealand Ltd
Wellington: T & W Young Building, 77—85 Customhouse Quay, 1
CPO Box 472

SOUTH AFRICA
Butterworth & Co (South Africa) (Pty) Ltd
Durban: 152—154 Gale Street

USA
Butterworth (Publishers) Inc
Boston: 19 Cummings Park, Woburn, Mass. 01801

First Published 1978
    reprinted 1979

© Jack Bowyer, 1978

British Library Cataloguing in Publication Data

Bowyer, Jack
    Building technology.
    1.
    1. Building
    1. Title
    690   TH145   77—30272

ISBN 0—408 00298 0

Typeset by Butterworths Litho Preparation Department

Printed in England by The Whitefriars Press Ltd,
    London and Tonbridge

Contents

INTRODUCTION   1

MODULE A   THE BUILDING INDUSTRY   1

1.00   Pattern of the built environment   1
2.00   The building team   2
3.00   Sources of work and finance   3
4.00   Constraints and statutory controls   4
5.00   Contract procedure and documentation   5

MODULE B   SITE INVESTIGATION, SETTING OUT AND PLANT   7

6.00   Site selection   7
7.00   Site investigation   8
   7.01 }
   7.02 } Methods   8
   7.03 } Types of subsoil and permissable
   7.04 } loading   9
   7.05 Loading from building structures   10
   7.06 Types of building site   10
8.00   Setting out and site levels   10
   8.01 }
   8.02 } Datum   10
   8.03 Building lines   11
   8.04 }
   8.05 } Methods of squaring up buildings   12
9.00   Site preparation and plant   12
   9.01 Removal of top soil   13
   9.02 Water for building purposes 13
   9.03 Site accommodation   13
   9.04 Site security   13
   9.05 }
   9.06 } Plant   13

MODULE C   BUILDING ELEMENTS' PRACTICE AND MATERIALS   15

10.00   Constituent parts and building elements — substructure and superstructure   15
   10.01 Functional elements   15
   10.02 Primary elements   15
   10.03 Secondary elements   15
   10.04 }
   10.05 } Finishings 15
11.00   Factors affecting the choice and fundamentals of construction and materials   16
   11.01 Associated production centres   16
   11.02 Factors affecting methods of construction   16
   11.03 }
   11.04 } Finance   16

11.05   Basic construction alternatives for 2—3 storey domestic structures   16
       Single-storey factory or warehouse
       Multi-storey framed projects
11.06   Basic building materials   17
       Sand and ballast
       Cement
       Bricks
       Blocks
       Steel
       Timber

MODULE D   THE SUBSTRUCTURE OF BUILDING   20

12.00   Substructure — primary function and constituent parts   20
   12.01 }
   12.02 } Loadings   20
   12.03 } Problems of underlying subsoils and
   12.04 } filling   20, 21
   12.05 Soluble sulphates in subsoils   21
   12.06 Clay subsoils   21
   12.07 Basic requirements of foundations   21
   12.08 Requirements of Building Regulations   21
13.00   Foundations — brick walls and partitions   23
   13.01 Angle of repose of subsoil   23
   13.02 }
   13.03 } Planing and strutting   23
   13.04 Excavation of large areas   24
   13.05 Sheet piling and excavation shoring   24
   13.06 Removal of ground water   24
   13.07 Preparation of foundation bottoms   24
   13.08 Checking thickness of foundation concrete   24
   13.09 }
   13.10 } Brickwork in foundations   26
   13.11 Alternative foundations to domestic buildings   26
       Reinforced concrete raft
       Short bored piles
       Deep strip foundations
       Wide strip foundations
   13.12 Foundations to load bearing partitions   27
   13.13 Support to non loadbearing partitions   28

14.00   Foundations — steel columns and isolated piers   28
    14.01   Reinforcement   28
    14.02   Mortices for foundation bolts   28
    14.03   Grouting to bolts and base plates   28
    14.04   Offset foundations to brick piers   28
15.00   Resistance to rising damp   28
    15.01   Construction of walls and floors   29
    15.02   Continuity   29
    15.03   Filling under solid concrete slabs   29
    15.04   Oversize concrete slabs   29
    15.05   Level in relationship to perimeter ground level   30
    15.06   Damp-proof membranes   30
    15.07 }
    15.08 } Damp proof courses of walls and partitions   30
    15.09   Reasons for faults in dpc's   31

MODULE E   THE SUPERSTRUCTURE OF BUILDING   32

16.00   Superstructure — primary functions   32
    16.01   Structural stability   32
    16.02   Fire resistance and spread of flame   32
    16.03 }
    16.04 } Walls, floors and roofs   33
    16.05   Periods of fire resistance   33
    16.06 }
    16.07 } Durability and weather resistance 33
    16.08   Protection against damp — Building Regulation requirements   34
    16.09   Thermal and sound resistance   35
    16.10   Condensation   35
    16.11   Thermal insulation — Building Regulation requirements   35
    16.12   Sound insulation — Building Regulation requirements   36
    16.13   Other functions for consideration 36
17.00   Scaffolding and temporary support   37
    17.01   Materials for scaffolding   37
    17.02   Platforms and walkways   37
    17.03   Types of scaffold and access   38
    17.04   Temporary supports   38
    17.05   Flying shores   38
    17.06   Raking shores   39
    17.07   Needle, prop and strut   39
    17.08   Strutting to adjacent openings   39
18.00   Function and construction of external brick walls   39
    18.01   Damp proof courses   39
    18.02   Materials for dpc's   40
    18.03   Ineffectual dpc's   41
    18.04   Building Regulations — 'Deemed to satisfy' construction   41
          Bonding

18.05   Raking back, tooth and bond   42
          Block bonding
18.06   Weather resistance   43
18.07   Cavity walls   43
18.08   Thermal resistance   43
18.09   External appearance — alternative facing materials   43
18.10   Wall ties   44
18.11   Mortars   44
          Jointing and pointing
18.12   Types of mortar   45
18.13   Finishing joists   45
19.00   Openings in external walls   45
    19.01   Lintols and reveals — stability and sequence of construction   46
    19.02 }
    19.03 } Sills   46
    19.04   Reveals   47
    19.05 }
    19.06 } Lintols   48, 49
    19.07 }
    19.08   Window boards   49
20.00   Internal walls and partitions   50
    20.01   Factors governing section of materials   51
          Brick
          Concrete block
          Timber stud
          Proprietory partitions
    20.02   Bonding and mortars for structural partitions   52
    20.03   Lintols over openings   52
          Problems of differential shrinkage
          Key for plaster
    20.04   Precast or *insitu* concrete lintols   52
          Mild steel arch bars
          Galvanised pressed steel
21.00   Timber flooring   53
    21.01   CP and BS requirements for timber   53
    21.02   Treatment of timber against decay and infestation   53
    21.03   Suspended timber ground floors   54
    21.04   Sleeper walls   54
    21.05   Timber floors on oversite concrete slabs   55
    21.06   Timber upper floors   55, 56
          Support and protection
          Joist hangers
    21.07   Strutting   56
    21.08   Size of timber and selection   56
    21.09   Materials for floor surfacing   56
    21.10   Finishing and protection of surfacing materials   57
22.00   Roof construction — primary functions   57
    22.01   Design of roof structure   57

22.02 Pitch 57
     Loading
     Building Regulations − size of timbers
     and selection
22.03 Materials for weathering 58
     Plain tiles
     Pantiles
     Interlocking tiles
     Slates
22.04 Principles of traditional pitched roof
     construction 58
     Hips and valleys
22.05 Types of traditional timber pitched
     roofs 59
     Single roofs − lean-to
     Couple roof
     Close couple roof
     Collar roof
     Double roofs
22.06 Timber trusses with plate con-
     nectors 61
     Gang nail trusses
     Trussed rafters
22.07 Trussed purlins 62
22.08 Sarking felt 62
22.09 Roofing battens 62
22.10 Tiling and slating terms 62
     Margin
     Lap
     Gauge
     Head and centre nailing
22.11 Eaves 63
22.12 Verges to gables 63
     Undercloak courses
22.13 Ridges and ridge tiles 63
22.14 Hips and hip tiles 64
22.15 Valleys, valley tiles and lead
     valley construction 64
22.16 Insulation of domestic roofs 64
22.17 Flat roofs − primary functions 65
22.18 Building Regulations − size of timbers
     and selection 65
22.19 Problems of stormwater and falls 65
22.20 Decking to flat roofs and insulation
     66
22.21 Alternative decking materials 67
22.22 Verge details of timber flat roofs 67
22.23 Concrete flat roofs 67
     In situ with m.s. bar reinforcements
     In situ with EML reinforcement
22.24 Verge and abutment details to
     concrete flat roofs 68
22.25 Weathering materials for flat roofs 68
     Bitumen felt
     Asphalt

22.26 Removal of rainwater 68
     Pitched roof construction
     Flat roof construction
22.27 Rain water gutters 70
22.28 Rain water pipes 70
23.00 Low rise steel frames − design and fabrication
     requirements 70
    23.01 Structural steel profiles and
          sections 70
    23.02 Bolting and welding 71
    23.03 Design alternatives 71
          Portal frame
          Post and truss
    23.04 Two and three storey frames 72
    23.05 Stanchions and base plates 73
    23.06 Fire resistance 73
    23.07 Corrosion 74
    23.08 Cladding − Building Regulation
          requirements regarding fire
          resistance 74

Appendix: Building Standards (Scotland) Regulations
         1971−1975 75

Acknowledgement

The publishers wish to thank Messrs. JCB Sales Ltd. and The Liner Engineering Co. Ltd. for permission to illustrate their earth moving and concrete plant

Bibliography and references

MODULE A

History of Building, Jack Bowyer, Crosby Lockwood
Architect's Job Book, RIBA Publications Ltd
The Building Regulations 1976, HMSO
The Building Standards (Scotland) (Consolidation) *Regulations, 1971–75* HMSO
Explanatory Memorandum to the Regulations (Scotland) 1972–75, HMSO
Small Works Contract Documentation, Jack Bowyer, The Architectural Press Ltd.

MODULE B

CP 2001: 1957 *Site investigations*
BS 1377: 1967 *Methods of testing soils for engineering purposes*
BRS Digests 63, 64 and 67, Soils and Foundations
The CIRIA Manual of Setting Out Procedures, Pitman
BRS Digest 114 (1970), *Accuracy in setting-out*
CP 3: Chapter V: Loading Pt. 1.: 1967 *Dead and imposed loads*, Pt. 2 *Wind loads*
CP 2003: 1959 *Earthworks*
BS 3148: 1959 *Tests for water for making concrete*
Health and Safety at Work Act, HMSO

MODULE C

BS 882: 1965 *Aggregates from natural sources for concrete*
BS 12: 1958 Pt. 2. 1971 *Portland Cement*
BS 3921: Pt. 2. 1969 *Clay bricks*
BS 187: Pt. 2. 1970 *Sand lime bricks*
BS 1180: 1972 *Concrete bricks*
BS 4: Pt. 1. 1972 *Hot rolled steel sections*
      Pt. 2. 1969 *Hot rolled hollow steel sections*
BS 449: Pt. 1. 1970 *The use of structural steel in building*
BS 4449: 1969 *Hot rolled steel bars for the reinforcement of concrete*
BS 4483: 1969 *Steel fabric for the reinforcement of concrete*
CP 112: *The use of structural timber*
BS 4978: 1973 *Timber grades for structural use*
BS 4072: 1974 *Wood preservation by water borne compositions*
Forest Products Research Laboratory, Technical Note No. 25 *Stress Grading of Timber*

MODULE D

CP 101: 1972 *Foundations and substructures*
CP 2004: 1972 *Foundations*
CP 110 Pt. 1: 1972 *The structural use of concrete – design, materials and workmanship*

CP 114 Pt. 2: 1969 *The structural use of reinforced concrete in buildings*
Cement and Concrete Association – *Concrete practice* (1975)
BRS Current Paper 58/68, D.C. Teychenne; *Specification of concrete*
BRS Digest 13. *Concrete mix proportioning and control* (Second Series)
BRS Digest 42. *Short bored pile foundations* (First Series)
NHBC, *Preventing foundation failures in new dwellings*

MODULE E

Principles of modern building 1970, HMSO
BS 648: 1964 *Schedule of weights of building materials*
BS 476 Pt. 8: 1972 *Fire tests on building materials and structures*
BRS Digest 127. *Index of exposure to driving rain*
BRS Digest 33. *The courses of damp in buildings*
BRS Digest 27. *Rising damp in walls* (second series)
BRS Digest 108. *Standardised U-values*
BRS Digest 128. *Insulation against external noise*
BRS Digest 102. *Sound insulation of traditional buildings*
CP 97 Pt. 1. 1967 *Common scaffolds in steel*
Construction (Working Places) Regulations, *Scaffolding*, HMSO
BS 743: 1970 *Materials for damp proof courses*
CP 121 Pt. 1. 1973 *Walling of brick or blockwork*
BRS Digest 61. *Strength of brick or block walls, etc*
BS 1243: 1972 *Metal ties for cavity wall construction*
BRS Digest 58. *Mortars for jointing*
BS 1198–1200: 1955 *Sands for mortar*
BS 4022: 1970 *Prefabricated gypsum wallboard panels*
BS 1230: 1970 *Gypsum plasterboard*
CP 142 Pt. 2.: 1971 *Slating and tiling*
BS 402 Pt. 2.: 1970 *Clay plain roofing tiles and fittings*
BS 473, 550 Pt. 2.: 1971 *Concrete plain roofing tiles and fittings*
BS 4471 Pt. 2.: 1971 *Wood battens for slating and tiling*
BS 747 Pt. 2: 1968 *Roofing felts*
CP 3 Chapter 2: *Thermal insulation*
CP 144 Pt. 3: 1970 *Built-up bitumen felt roofing*
CP 144 Pt. 4: 1970 *Mastic asphalt*
BS 1579: 1960 *Connectors for timber*
CP 308 *Drainage of roofs and paved areas*
BRS Digests 188 and 189
BS 460: 1964 *Cast iron rainwater goods*
BS 569: 1973 *Asbestos cement rainwater goods*
BS 4576: Pt. 1: 1970 *PVC rainwater goods*

Introduction

The introduction of the Technician Education Council Standard Units for Construction Technology has caused the whole basis of teaching in this subject to be drastically revised. This is due to a number of factors the principal being

(a) the time available for class contact and evaluation has been reduced to 60 hours per session. This is approximately half that previously available for ONC teaching in this subject;

(b) much of the old syllabus has been collated and included in separate subject units and therefore the wider scope for explanation and practical project work is now no longer controlled within the time available for the Construction Technology Unit.

In the preparation of *Building Technology 1 and 2*, the extent to which the range of alternative solutions to construction problems should be carried out has been carefully considered. It has been decided to omit much of what has, in the past, been considered as general practice and to concentrate on expanding and detailing good sound modern practice. For example, the construction of brick turned arches and accompanying centering has been omitted, together with first floor fireplace construction. In their place opportunity has been taken to explain the problems of condensation and its avoidance, to incorporate a number of modern timber jointing and strengthening techniques and to include modern methods of flue construction for stoves and boilers. Other divergencies from traditional techniques will be apparent to the informed reader.

The two volumes within the parameters outlined in this introduction, cover the first two years syllabus of the student in Building Technology.

Building Technology 1 covers the introduction to the subject and the construction of the superstructures of small domestic and single storey steel framed buildings.

Building Technology 2 deals with the provision and installation of joinery, services and simple drainage, finishing trades and external roads and footpaths and preparation for landscaping.

It is considered that by preparing the books in this way the logical development of a building can best be described to the junior student.

Reference has been made to other TEC units. Where essential to the proper understanding of a constructural element a brief explanation is included into the relevant module to integrate the two; technical aspects being omitted in favour of the specific subject unit. It is therefore essential that the following units be considered both complimentary and essential to the proper understanding of Construction Technology.

1. *Construction drawing 1 (TEC U75/049)*

2. *Site Surveying and Levelling 2 (TEC U75/056)*
   In respect of the preparation of site surveys and levels and detailed setting out by optical methods.

3. *Organisation and Procedures 1 (TEC U75/071)*
   Includes details of contracts and contractural documentation, British Standards and Codes of Practice, general information on the building professions and building legislation.

4. *Science and Materials 2 (TEC U75/042)*
   Includes detailed consideration of a wide variety of subjects including theoretical problems of sound and thermal insulation, structure and defects of wood, selection of aggregates, manufacture and testing of concrete defects and strengths of bricks blocks, plasters and paints films and the theory of corrosion.

The construction of modern buildings is almost wholly controlled by the directions and deemed to satisfy conditions contained within the Building Regulations and parallel legislation. As it is essential that the student should, from the beginning of his studies, understand and relate these requirements to his constructional studies care has been taken to relate the text directly to the relevant paragraphs in the Regulations e.g. (D3) general requirements on foundations. In addition, wherever possible previous references to detailed explanation is cross referenced in the text by noting the particular paragraph e.g. (7.03) division of subsoils into main groups.

Changes in technician education have also taken place in Scotland with the introduction of Scottish Technical Education Council (SCOTEC) certificate courses for building technicians. These courses have not adopted the modular approach of TEC but they do broadly include the same subject matter. Scottish students will find these two volumes cover practically all the topics of Introduction to Building at Stage I and Construction II at Stage II of the SCOTEC Certificate in Building.

Main references to building regulations within the text relate to The Building Regulations 1976 which do not apply in Scotland. Construction of buildings in Scotland is covered by the Building Standards (Scotland) (Consolidation) Regulations 1971–75. This fact is recognised in these books by the inclusion of asterisks which relate to equivalent sections of Scottish regulations listed in the Appendix. In addition, where Scottish practice differs significantly from English practice this is indicated.

It is hoped that the emphasis on practical and positive detailing will assist in providing the student coming fresh into the building industry from secondary education with a clear and positive identification with the essentials of good construction.

Module A The Building Industry

1.00 Pattern of the built environment

The preoccupations of early men were hunting and
food gathering and the social unit was the family.
Shelter from the elements was obtained from caves or
rock shelters easily defended from natural predators.
As the population slowly increased and man became
more adventurous in his wanderings, temporary
shelters of branches and leaves were constructed in
hunting areas where protection could be found during
protracted forays. In the course of time these shelters
took on a permanent form and, where timber was in
short supply, stones were gathered and built into
rough structures to provide simple walls roofed with
timber poles and rough thatch. Families began to
congregate in favoured areas for protection and to
build their huts around a common meeting place.

These first settlements date from about 13 000
B.C. and it is from this period that the first forest
clearings for agricultural purposes were made. This
process of domestication entered a second phase
some 3000 years later with the commencement of
the domestication of herd animals for power and
transport as well as food. The village with its fields
and small garden plots, barns and storage pits became
mostly self supporting, an economic state which in
Britain lasted until well into the nineteenth century.

1.01

In Western Europe city development began on the
island of Crete in the Eastern Mediterranean. Here the
fertile volcanic soil supported a high level of agricultural activity. With the possession of a powerful navy,
fortifications were unnecessary and trade, being protected, flourished between Crete and adjoining
countries. The association of high agricultural production and active trade continued to promote the
growth of cities throughout the Egyptian, Greek and
Roman civilisations. During this period the standard
of building advanced dramatically both in technical
content and aesthetic quality. The decline and eventual
destruction of the Roman civilisation led to a check
in the development of urban communities which
lasted until the 12th century AD.

1.02

The early mediaeval town was still basically dependent
on the surrounding countryside both for its food and
for much of its work. Industries in the town depended
for custom on the requirements of the local farmers,
many of whom either lived in the town or employed
labour from its population. The most important
feature of the town was the encircling wall built for
defence and enclosing streets lined with rows of
timber houses, each with its garden at the rear, often
planted with fruit trees and aromatic herbs. The
centre of the town was occupied by an open space,
primarily for the use of the weekly market but also
providing for assembly of the population at times of
trouble or at festivals. The church, market hall and
inns occupied frontages and the remainder was given
up to merchants and master craftsmen who, living
above their premises, opened up the ground floor
for the manufacture and display of their goods.

1.03

The invention of the cannon and the introduction of
the spoked wheel rapidly destroyed the concept of
the mediaeval town with its defensive walls and
narrow pedestrian orientated streets. The formation
of mobile national armies operating and fighting in
open country with large numbers of cannon caused
city walls to become obselete. Fast driven horse drawn
vehicles needed wide streets for effective use. Great
avenues were carved through the old mediaeval cities
and their frontages were rebuilt in classical styles
drawn from Roman examples popularised by the new
Renaissance principles. Behind these facades, however,
the old city life continued in the narrow streets and
largely insanitary buildings which survived. Due to
the difficulties both of obtaining premises and
trading, many craftsmen left the larger towns and
cities and set up their workshops in small country
towns, especially in the South of England and the
Cotswolds, creating not only a rebirth of activity but
also considerable wealth to wherever they moved.

1.04

During the 18th and 19th centuries vast areas of the
world's surface were opened up for settlement by the
land-hungry masses of Europe. New crops and a sur-
plus of grain led to an increase both of mercantile
activity and of population, villages grew into towns
and towns into cities. New urban complexes developed

to process imported raw materials and to house those who worked in the new factories. There were no statutory restraints and very few standards; the juxtaposition of factories, housing and commercial premises was a feature of these new industrial cities. The old cities continued to deteriorate and much of the new development was constructed with little consideration of health or sanitary conditions. Those who could afford to move from the city centres did so and there were created new suburbs outside the city where conditions were more tolerable. Unfortunately the city expansion continued and in many cases overwhelmed the new suburbs and their qualities decayed. The introduction of railway transport enabled their former inhabitants to seek dwellings further afield, commuting daily to the city centres for their daily business.

1.05

In the present century the problems of transport and the commuter have caused a revolution in the urban environment. The growth of motor vehicle ownership has led to a gradual usurpation by road transport of the railways' role in passenger transport. Wide motorways have slashed through city outskirts bringing cars at high speed direct to the centre, creating at the same time insuperable parking problems. The growth of concern over public health has generated the need for large public works utilities for the collection and disposal of both sewage and rubbish. An ever increasing expenditure on welfare has brought about the provision of general and specialised hospital facilities and office buildings to house staffs dealing with pensions and supplementary payments. A growing population requires both housing, schools and further education facilities, entertainment and recreational complexes in addition to retail stores to supply the necessities of life and factories and offices to provide employment.

In addition to the rebuilding and enlargement of existing towns and cities, new urban areas have been created in rural areas to provide for the overspill of population. To the original garden cities of the early decades of this century have been added nearly thirty new towns mostly planned around small nuclei of existing buildings. Many of these have become established as viable urban centres, some have not.

2.00 The building team

Before 1800, most buildings were constructed by the process of bringing together a number of craftsmen under the supervision of a surveyor who, after preparing simple drawings sufficient for the purpose, obtained estimates for the particular craft work included and then set his team to work. So long as

all buildings were wholly constructed of well tried materials and services such as electrical, plumbing and heating installations were unknown, this system worked well. During the last 150 years or so, the size of building projects has tended to increase and the complexity of construction and installed services has grown out of all recognition. Consequently methods for arranging the erection of buildings have tended to alter and develop until today we have reached a degree of complexity which would once never have been considered possible.

2.01

The building team today incorporates four distinct sections, each responsible for its own particular function in creating a building or building complex, each utilising its own particular expertise to further that end.

(a) The erection of a building must be in response to an actual need, either explicitly, e.g. the construction of a house or factory for the occupation of one person or company, or in response to an implied need which requires to be stimulated or created, e.g. the construction of a shopping unit or office block for which a tenant must be found. A third reason for the construction of a building or creation of an urban complex is the replacement of old outworn buildings by new. In addition there are numerous alteration and extension works, all of which require stimulation to start the work. The person or persons who give this initial impetus is *The Client*.

The client is responsible, whether as an individual, company, corporation or government department, for assessing and deciding on the degree of need for a particular building, for making arrangements for and providing suitable finance and for the appointment of professional advisers necessary to translate the need into a tangible possibility. In addition the client may well provide the site for the works and explicit instructions as to the precise nature of his requirements.

(b) The professional advisers usually necessary to translate the client's requirements into practical terms are threefold:

(i) The initiative is taken by *the architect*, appointed by the client direct, to prepare initial proposals for the required development and then to translate the design drawings into a series of production drawings. These fulfil a number of functions; firstly to enable approvals to be obtained under building control and planning regulations; secondly to enable bills of quantities to be prepared for pricing by the builder's estimator in support of a tender; and thirdly to enable the building to be constructed. To this end the architect will generally advise the client on the employment of specialist professionals to assist him, employed and paid by the client but under the direction of the architect whose duty it is to co-ordinate and incorporate their work into his own drawings and schedules. In addition the architect is required to ensure that the conditions of the contract are kept by both signatories, e.g. client and contractor, that the work is generally in accordance with the contract provisions and to certify payment on account as laid down in the contract provisions.

(ii) The preparation of the document known as the bill of quantities is carried out by the *quantity surveyor*. This specialist surveyor measures the material and labour content of the building works from drawings and other information prepared and supplied by the architect, incorporating these into a document prepared in accordance with an agreed form known as the Standard Method of Measurement. This document is priced in the contractor's office to produce a valuation of the total cost of the work which is tendered or offered to the architect for consideration by the client. In addition the quantity surveyor carries out valuations to enable the architect to certify regular payments and in due course, at the end of the contract, prepares the basis of the statement of final account which is presented by the architect to the client.

(iii) Most buildings of any size have structural problems which require the services of a professional *structural engineer* to analyse the various alternatives and prepare, under the direction of the architect and in conjunction with his drawings, structural calculations and design drawings for the frame of the building. In addition most structural engineers advise on the tenders submitted for the specialist steel or reinforced concrete work and carry out inspections during the progress of the contract to ensure that the work is being carried out in accordance with the structural design details.

Some buildings incorporate electrical or mechanical installations of great complexity. These services need not only specialist designers but also co-ordination to ensure that they are provided as efficiently and safely as possible. Appointed by the client and working under the direction of the architect, *electrical* and *mechanical engineering consultants* prepare both calculations and design drawings on the basis of the architect's proposals to enable quotations to be obtained from specialist contractors for these works. In addition these consultants carry out regular inspections to ensure that the work is installed satisfactorily in accordance with their designs.

(c) The end product of professional activity in the building industry is the construction of the building itself and this is placed in the hands of the *building contractor*. The bill of quantities for the preparation of the tender is passed by the contractor to his estimator who computes the cost of each item and enters this in the appropriate section of the document. If the tender is successful and the contract won, the contractor will generally employ a number of staff to control the work. If the contract is of reasonable size, he will place a contracts manager in charge with perhaps a junior surveyor to measure and value the work for the contractor's office. In charge of the site works itself will be the foreman or site agent and manager, responsible for the correct interpretation of drawings, quantities and specification of works and for the control of materials and labour. He may have separate trade foremen under his charge responsible for their separate trades and also a ganger responsible for the general labourers and for moving equipment, plant and materials as required.

(d) Works of a specialist nature are generally carried out by firms usually nominated by the architect and employed on his instructions by the contractor as nominated sub-contractors. These firms carry out such work as the supply and erection of structural steelwork, electrical and heating installations and specialist roofing. In addition, many contractors themselves employ specialist firms direct for plastering, plumbing and similar trades and these are also known as sub-contractors although they are not employed on the architect's instructions.

(e) The inspection of large contracts to ensure the works are in accordance with the contract is generally placed in the hands of a *clerk of works*. He is appointed and paid by the employer on the architect's nomination and carries out his duties under the control of the architect, keeping records of variations from the contract works, ensuring materials and workmanship are as the contract dictates, keeping records of men employed on the site, the state of the weather and any stoppages. He also agrees items of a general nature direct with the foreman and sees that the architect's instructions are properly carried out. In addition, the building control officer makes regular inspections to ensure that the work conforms to the Building Regulations.

3.00 Sources of work and finance

A number of sources of work for the building industry have already been described. These fluctuate considerably in value and have been greatly affected in the past thirty years by economic as well as Governmental pressures. All, however, depend on the supply and flow of money and with such enormous sums in direct governmental control, the dependance of the building industry on political whims has become of great significance.

3.01
Central control of building industry growth is virtually complete in public housing, education, hospitals and medical centres, new towns and much rehabilitation works in city centres. Most if not all capital for these projects is by Government grant for new works, although in some cases maintenance work which forms an increasing volume of turnover in terms of cash value is paid for from revenue such as rates. In recent years, this central control of finance has been responsible for considerable variations in building work load which has not helped the industry to maintain steady and efficient growth.

3.02
Outside public building works, finance is provided either from private sources, including company profits, bank loans or building society mortgages. A feature of building finance which has provided funds for many large projects is from surpluses from insurance and pension funds and the system by which a newly constructed building is bought from its owners by a finance corporation and leased back at an annual rental.

3.03
With finance assured, the sources of work for the building industry are varied and all-embracing. Reference has been made to various types of client organisations who commission work. Recently, with a fall off in home demand, the industry has been forced to look abroad for its work and many professional consultants and contractors have been actively engaged in Europe and the Middle East. A great deal of work is still carred on in Commonwealth and former colonial countries.

4.00 Constraints and statutory controls*
Statutory control of building in Britain commenced in 1189 AD when, after a series of disastrous fires, Henry Fitz-Alwyn, first Mayor of London, promulgated the London Assize, the first Code of Byelaws relating to town planning and the construction of buildings. Its principal aim was to reduce the risk of fire spreading from one property to another by the provision of stone party walls. From this important beginning further legislation was enacted over the next six hundred years, mostly concerned with the prevention of the spread of fire by the improvement of construction and environment. One of the most important of these was The Act for the Rebuilding of the City of London — 1667 — after the great fire of the previous year.

4.01
The problems of practical control were always difficult for the mayor and aldermen of London due to the sheer size of the task. These were solved, in theory at least, by the Building Act of 1774 which empowered the City Council to appoint district surveyors to ensure building works were carried out in accordance with the provisions of the Act. For the first time houses were divided into groups according to their area but this procedure was not particularly satisfactory and the Act of 1844 amended designation into classes of occupation. In addition, for the first time halls, corridors and staircases of public buildings had to be made fireproof for the safety of the general public.

4.02
All these Acts referred to building work in the City of London. In 1848 the first Public Health Act came into effect bringing modern sanitary law into being. In the previous year the Town Improvement Clauses Act had authorised the appointment 'of a person duly qualified to act as a local surveyor of paving, drainage etc.' and this provision was embodied in the second Public Health Act of 1875. All this legislation, prepared for the City of London, needed to be extended to other towns and cities of Britain and this was effected by the Local Government Act of 1858.

4.03
The Public Health Act of 1936 included New Model Byelaws, prepared to include new methods of construction relative to any reasonable form of building, to ensure that this was not hampered by the operation of restrictive building byelaws. Each Local Authority was empowered to omit or select from the Model Byelaws in consideration of the conditions prevailing in their district and base their new byelaws on the appropriate model clauses. These byelaws continued in force for nearly thirty years. (*Note.* Some parts of the Act relating to Building Control do not apply in Scotland)

4.04

In 1965 a new form of building control was enacted. The Building Regulations 1965 came into effect on 1st February 1966 and with a number of amendments are in force today in England and Wales, Scotland having its own special version*. The Regulations are wide ranging covering all aspects of building from protection against fire, structural stability, sound transmission, drainage and sanitary conveniences and fitness of materials etc. Continuous reference is made throughout to various Codes of Practice and British Standard Specifications which lay down minimum standards of material and workmanship which are deemed satisfactory under the provisions of the Building Regulations.

4.05

During the 1930's, the need for some form of development control became apparent as much unsatisfactory exploitation of the countryside and coastal areas took place. Immediately after the 1939-45 war the drafting of legislation to control development was put in hand, culminating in the Town and Country Planning Act 1947 which came into full force and effect on 1st July 1948. Provision for statutory control is provided in the Act and in view of its wide reaching powers conferring the right of making subordinate rules, regulations, orders and directions on the Minister in charge, the Act and its operation have led to a number of serious anomalies in approval and appeal decisions. These have caused much concern to the professional bodies whose members are concerned with applications for development approval under the Act.

Separate but similar Town and Country Planning Acts apply to Scotland.

5.00 Contract procedure and documentation

The majority of building contracts follow similar patterns from start to finish, whether they are for very large or for relatively small buildings. Generally it is only in the time taken for the various stages to be completed that there is any variation. Some of these stages have been mentioned in passing in connection with other matters.

5.01

The first step in any contract is the invitation by a prospective building client to an architect to act for him in the construction of a project or the alteration of an existing building. From this initial invitation the architect will obtain from his client a brief comprising as full details of his requirements as it is possible at that time to obtain. This will include details of the site, its location and area, restrictions laid down by the Planning Authority, etc. The survey of the site is then prepared, including taking levels of both the site and the surrounding roads and footpaths. From the information obtained from the brief and the survey the architect will prepare firstly a feasibility study to see if the client's proposals are capable of fullfillment and then a sketch design to illustrate, graphically, his interpretation of the client's requirements. These designs may be amended several times before the client's requirements are fully met and then agreed with the local planning authority during informal discussions with the architect. It is at this point that an application for approval under the Town and Country Planning Acts is usually made.

5.02

If the project requires specialist structural advice a copy of the sketch plans with explanatory details is then sent to the consultant structural engineer for his proposals. When these are finalised, the details and layout form the basis of the structure and the architect's production drawings are based on and worked up around the information obtained. At the same time, if the project includes mechanical services of any size, the drawings and details will be sent to a consultant mechanical engineer for details of a suitable system and builders work necessary in ducts, boiler and tank rooms which must be included in the production drawings.

5.03

Cost is a vital ingredient in all building contracts and the quantity surveyor will be invited to prepare preliminary estimates of cost from the sketch plans for submission to the client with the drawings themselves. If the initial costings are approved, continuous monitoring must be applied to ensure that the project costs do not soar during the preparation of production drawings and subsequent bills of quantities.

5.04

On completion of production drawings, these are submitted to the local Building Control for approval. At the same time copies complete with schedules of finishings, doors and windows etc. and the draft specification of works are sent to the quantity surveyor to enable him to commence preparation of the bills of quantities.

In small or relatively simple contracts, bills of quantities are often unnecessary. The specification is then used in conjunction with full drawings to enable the builder's estimator to prepare a tender for the work. In addition to standard clauses concerned with the protection of the work under construction, proper insurance of the building, provision of plant, water, etc, the specification includes careful and complete descriptions of all materials and standards of workmanship needed in the proposed work.

The bills of quantities are similar in content but, as their name implies, they include all precise quantities of the materials to be used. In a large building this enables estimators to complete the pricing of exactly similar documents more quickly than would be the case if each had to prepare his own quantities first.

5.05

Tenders are invited, therefore, either with the issue of complete drawings and specification or by the provision of a bill of quantities and such drawings as are necessary to explain the extent and scope of the work to the contractors tendering for the contract. Full drawings may be inspected by the contractor in the architect's office, if required, by appointment.

Tenders, being the amount of money required by a contractor to carry out the work shown on the tendering drawings and documents, are usually returned to the architect who opens them usually in the presence of the client, sometimes with the contractors present. It is usual to recommend the lowest tender for acceptance. On acceptance, a contract is prepared between the client (who now is called the 'Employer') and the contractor and is signed by both parties. A date for possession of the site by the contractor and commencement of the works is then agreed and incorporated in the contract, together with the date for completion of the works.

On possession of the site, the contractor will set up his sheds and store huts and, after setting out the position and extent of the work, commence his excavations from drawings and copies of the bills of quantities and specifications provided for the purpose by the architect. He will arrange for the supply and delivery to site of all materials necessary for the works, take on such labour as he thinks necessary, enter into sub-contracts with specialist contractors for the carrying out of work as directed by the architect and carry on the works at a proper rate bearing in mind the date for completion. At intervals the architect will inspect the work to see that this is proceeding generally in accordance with the contract and answer any queries which may arise and give instructions in connection with the works, materials or workmanship. At intervals the value of work carried out is assessed and a certificate is issued stating the agreed value. This is sent to the contractor who is responsible for forwarding the certificate to the employer for payment. A small percentage of the value certified is retained against the contractor's failure to complete his contractual obligations.

On completion of the works, the architect will issue a certificate to the effect that, in his opinion, practical completion has been reached and the employer takes possession of the building. Immediately half the percentage of value retained is released and paid to the contractor. Any defects which occur now for a period (usually six months) defined in the contract and for which the contractor is responsible must be put right at his sole cost. These defects are included in a schedule prepared by the architect immediately before the end of this maintenance period and sent to the contractor for rectification. In the meantime the preparation of the final account has been progressing and as soon as this is agreed and the maintenance items completed by the contractor the balance of any monies due to the contractor are included in the final certificate issued for settlement by the employer.

Module B Site Investigation, Setting out and Plant

6.00 Site selection
The increasingly high cost of building land necessitates great care in its selection for development. Planning controls can also have a limiting effect and restrictions placed on access by road authorities can also have a severely restricting influence. In addition a number of important matters must be considered when selecting a site for building development.

6.01
The aspect of the site is often important. This will control the amount of sun which can be expected to fall on the building during the day. Southward facing sites are particularly favoured in this respect although with the sun facing into the building the view is often less clear than one towards the north. It is necessary to ensure that all habitable rooms receive some sunshine during the day at all periods of the year when the sun is shining. This should take into account that in Britain the maximum angle of the sun above the horizon varies between 15° in December to 62° at mid-summer.

6.02
The view from the site may well be of great importance to the developer. Sites with fine open views command high prices and are consequently much in demand.

6.03
Elevation should be considered as generally, elevated sites are better drained than low lying, which may not only be damp but also liable to flooding.

6.04
Climate is important, especially in connection with private residential accommodation where a warm sunny climate is preferred to a bleak colder situation.

6.05
Amenities and facilities provided either by private enterprise or by government and local authorities are considered to be essential to modern life. Public transport to local and national centres. shopping and educational facilities, sports and other recreational centres are all to be considered.

6.06
The subsoil of the site is important as it will either materially assist in keeping building costs down or so increase them as to render the development uneconomic. The factors which have to be taken into account are:

(i) Bearing value of subsoil — whether this is sufficient to carry the loads to be imposed on it without excessive foundation works.

(ii) Ease of excavation enabling trenches to be excavated with the minimum of labour and cost.

(iii) Angle of repose of subsoil — if this is acute the need for expensive temporary planking and strutting to maintain the sides of the excavation may be reduced.

(iv) Depth of subsoil and absence of any thin strata of unsatisfactory soils within the depth necessary to ensure stability of the overlying building structure.

(v) The presence or otherwise of any pockets of tipping or made up ground or the possibility of mining subsidence, all of which would entail expensive foundation works.

6.07
Mention has been made of low lying sites and also the problems of flooding. Usually these sites have a natural water table level very close to the surface, varying between winter and summer as rainfall and natural evaporation increase and decrease. In addition, sloping sites can have problems when the subsoil is rock and natural springs tend to flow down the upper surface immediately below the top soil. Sites which have either high water tables or are so situated as to carry a great deal of flowing ground water usually need subsoil drainage to reduce and control the problem (see *Building Technology 2*; section 23.00 *et seq*).

6.08
The cost of extending suitable services such as sewers, gas, water and electricity to serve a site may

be very expensive indeed. The existence of such services adjoining a site may be no evidence that either

(i) they are adequate to serve the proposed development without overloading the system to the detriment of other users, or

(ii) connection can be made to them to serve the development.

In addition, it may be necessary to provide facilities to the electricity board for the erection of a substation on the site to serve the development or ground levels may prohibit foul drains serving the site to be connected to the adjacent sewer. In this case a sewage plant or pumping facilities may be needed, all of which may well increase costs. These problems should be resolved at an early date.

6.09

Sites without proper or adequate access for pedestrians or vehicles to suit the proposed development are virtually valueless. Statutory road authorities lay down stringent requirements for the design of many types of vehicle access, especially to trunk roads and visibility splays have to be accommodated within the boundaries to the site road frontage.

6.10

Some sites have certain restrictions placed on them by legal restraints known as covenants. These covenants are written into the deeds of the property and may restrict the type or density of development. In addition adjoining owners may enjoy certain rights over the site such as rights of way or passage across the site to gain access to their own land or to draw or discharge water from or into existing ditches or streams.

All these factors must be taken into consideration in detail in the selection of a site for a particular development.

7.00 Site investigation

Much of the information needed to carry out a proper site selection can only be determined by a thorough investigation of the physical nature and composition of the actual site itself. This information will generally comprise:

(i) The nature and composition of the subsoil.

(ii) The presence of any filling or natural strata of less strength and cohesion than the bulk of the subsoil itself.

(iii) The presence of any variation in subsoil across the site due to the presence of natural fault lines or beds of material laid down by climatic conditions or natural features such as streams now no longer in existence.

(iv) The level of the existing water table at the date of the investigation and the presence of any springs or movement in the flow of ground water.

7.01

A number of methods may be utilised to determine the depth and composition of the subsoil of a building site. These vary with the size or complexity of the project and also the financial resources available for the investigation.

For small residential or similar projects it may be sufficient to determine the type and approximate bearing value of the subsoil by one of the following methods:

(i) By digging a number of small holes about 600 mm deep around the approximate perimeter of the proposed building.

(ii) By drilling a number of similar holes with a hand auger which produces a hole about 150 mm dia and when extracted produces a core or plug of the material through which the auger has passed.

(iii) By driving a pointed steel crowbar into the ground and gauging the degree of resistance to the bar.

Probably the best of these is the use of a hand auger to extract soil samples followed by the insertion of a crowbar to estimate the resistance of the subsoil to penetration at foundation depth.

7.02

For rather larger projects more expensive methods may be used:

(i) The excavation of a series of trial holes about 1m square x 1.5 m deep. The depth should be at least 0.5 m below the proposed level of any foundations to ensure that the subsoil strata penetrated is continuous. Driving a crowbar into the bottom for a further 0.5 m will assist in confirming this continuity. This method is relatively inexpensive, labour only being employed. Care must be taken to protect the excavation with a cover or enclosing fence to prevent anyone falling into the hole.

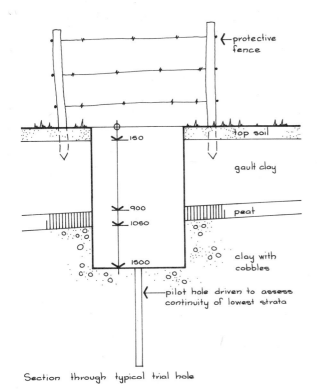

Name of job :		Warehouse for A. Client
Location :		Industrial Estate Newtown
Surveyor :		A. Tape
Description :		Site is level, close to old estuary and is at present down to grazing
Trial hole :	Section :	Type :
No. 1 ground level 150		vegetable loam and top soil
		firm gault clay
900 1050		fibrous peat
bottom of trial hole		firm gault clay incorporating round pebbles to 2·5m (assessed)

Section through typical trial hole

Specimen page of Site Investigation Report

(ii) By setting up a mechanical rig and drilling a hole either by percussion methods, which use a chisel pointed steel bit screwed to a steel rod, or by the use of a hollow tube which lifts a core of subsoil back up to the surface. These methods are used when the investigation is carried out at depths greater than those at which trial holes are economic.

(iii) By loading a reinforced concrete slab with increasing weights at 2 hourly intervals and levelling up the upper surface with an optical level. From the amount of settlement the bearing value of the subsoil can be calculated in relation to the area of the slab.

With open trial holes and extraction boring the precise level at which ground water is encountered can be determined by visual inspection and measurement.

Information gained from such investigations is recorded in a site investigation report for the use of the engineer in preparing his design for the foundations and substructure.

7.03*

Load bearing sub-soils can be generally divided into four main groups as follows:

(i) Rock subsoil such as sandstone, limestone or firm chalk. (Building Regulations Class I).

(ii) Non-cohesive soils such as dry compact gravel or compact uniform sand. (Building Regulations Class II).

(iii) Cohesive soils such as clay and sandy clay. (Building Regulations Classes III, IV, V and VI).

(iv) Very soft silt and silty clay. (Building Regulations Class VII).

7.04

Water may be a problem both with impermeable rock where ground water may be present in quantity at the junction of rock and overlying weathered soil and in gravels where the strata may be submerged in ground water. In the latter instance the permissible bearing pressure is reduced by half. In clay subsoils water can be a problem where the top 600-900 mm may swell with absorbed water and later shrink when the water dries out. Peat and waterlogged sands have little bearing strength and as settlement can be severe should never be used as a bearing strata without specialist

9

advice. The maximum bearing value allowable on various types of subsoils in kN/m² is as follows:

Subsoil	Type	Allowable bearing pressures in kN/m²
Rocks (Class I)	Limestone, sandstone, firm chalk	1000–4000
Non-cohesive soils (Class II)	Dry compact gravel, compact uniform sand	400 300
Cohesive soils	Stiff dry clay Firm sandy clay	300 200
	Soft sandy clay Very soft sandy clay or silt	100† 50†

† Under the Building Regulations, 'deemed to satisfy' clauses do not permit loads greater than 30 kN/m² for these subsoils (see also Appendix).

7.05

Although the weight of two and three storey domestic buildings and single storey steel frame buildings will vary in specific cases, approximate weights on foundations can be determined remembering that factors of safety are employed in determining bearing values. These weights can be assessed as follows:

Types of building	Approximate load/m run of foundation in kN
Domestic load bearing brickwork two stories in height	20
Three stories in height	30
Single storey steel framed building	50/100 on columns

7.06

There are three principal types of building site:

(i) Open fields where the top soil for many years has been cultivated to a depth of about 300 mm.

(ii) Wooded sites where similar depth of topsoil can be expected

(iii) Reclaimed urban sites which have been subjected to successive building and demolition for perhaps centuries.

There are few problems associated with the first type of site subject to the bearing quality of the subsoil and the presence or otherwise of a high water table. The second type of site poses more problems. Where trees have to be cut down in areas to be covered with buildings or roadworks, the whole of the root structure must be dragged out. It is not satisfactory for root growths which may continue to develop to be left in these positions. The excavations left must be properly filled in with hardcore, in layers not exceeding 225 mm thick and well watered in and consolidated by rolling or ramming.

Where trees are to be retained either under Tree Preservation Orders or because they are to be retained under the contract, they must be clearly shown on the drawings and care taken to keep their trunks and roots free from spoil heaps which can consolidate the subsoil around and kill the tree.

The third type of site can pose many problems. It is likely that the site has been filled in with hardcore which is probably loosely compacted and can contain large voids. It is also possible that old foundations and floor slabs will have been left in and need to be broken out. Drain runs and old service pipes will probably be found. It is essential that all these problems are fully appreciated and steps taken to deal with them if the occasion arrises. Usually it will be necessary to take foundations down to a level below that of any original work or filling encountered.

8.00 Setting out and site levels

Before production drawings of any building development can be finalised it is necessary for an accurate field survey to be prepared of the site. This will show the shape and position of perimeter boundaries, adjacent topographical features such as roads and buildings which are essential to the development, features such as trees, ditches and other natural obstructions on the site and the line of existing services. From the survey drawing produced from this information a grid will be laid down over the area of the site and, by the use of an optical instrument and a measuring staff, a series of spot levels are taken. From these levels the site contours can be plotted, each level calculated from a known datum point to enable later reference to be made and the levels transferred back to their original position on the site.

8.01

The datum mentioned must be taken from a permanent object, one which is unlikely to be moved for any purpose from the time the original levels are taken to their transference to the site works. The surveyors of the government Ordnance Survey transfer a number of their levels to points, mainly in urban areas, each point of which relates precisely to a prime datum at Newlyn in Cornwall. These datum are known as Ordnance Bench Marks (OBM) and their precise heights above datum at Newlyn are indicated on the large scale (1:1250 and 1:2500)

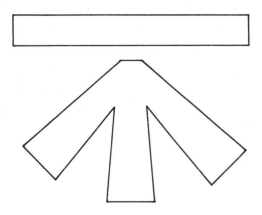

Illustration of Ordnance Bench Mark

ordnance survey plans which are on sale at specialist bookshops to the general public.

8.02

Most of these marks are to be found on boundary walls and plinths of churches and other public buildings. If it is not possible to refer the site levels to Ordnance Datum, a manhole cover in the road or a similar, easily identified, fixed and permanent object may be used and identified as datum, being provided with a notional value such as 100.00.

If the datum is not actually on the site it is necessary to transfer the datum from the original point to a new point within the boundaries of the site. Care must be taken to ensure that the level is not only preserved from damage but also can be retained for the whole period of the contract. A bolt or steel rod set to protrude above a block of concrete cast into the ground would be a good example of a temporary Bench Mark.

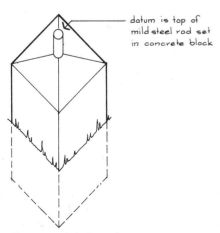

datum is top of mild steel rod set in concrete block

Temporary bench mark

8.03

The precise placing of the building on a site is usually controlled by building lines defined in the Highways Act 1959* as a 'frontage line for building'. The precise line may be prescribed by either the highway authority for the frontage onto the road or by the planning authority in respect of building lines parallel to side boundaries. Those building lines are taken into account by the architect in designing the building and dimensions are indicated on the site or layout drawings showing both the front building line and the position of at least one corner. From this information the basic lines can be set out on site. These should be checked and agreed with both the architect and the local authority before proceeding further.

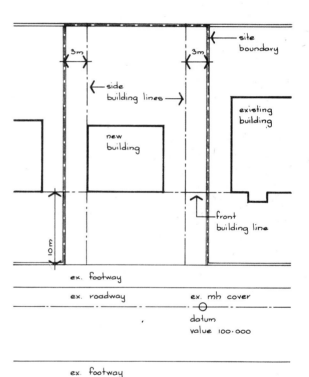

Site plan showing building lines and datum

8.04

With the main building line and one corner of the building established the flank walls can be set out at right angles by a number of methods:

(i) By using a large builder's square placed against the building line and the side line produced to the required length.

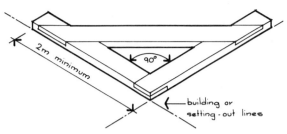

Setting out using large builder's timber square
constructed from 150 x 38 softwood

(ii) By using the 3:4:5 method (Pythagoras theorem).

(iii) By using a proprietory optical square which comprises two small sighting telescopes permanently set at precise right angles to one another.

(iv) By using an optical instrument with a base ring graduated to degrees and sighting along the angles required. This method is generally used when angles other than right angles from the corners of the building are involved.

8.05

To establish permanent line markers, horizontal boards known as 'profiles' secured to pegs driven into the ground are established in positions close to the planned corners of the building and where the principal walls will occur. The main building lines, centre lines and the spread of foundations are marked either by saw cuts or nails driven in at the right position and from these, excavations and brickwork in substructures can be accurately set out and constructed. A radius rod from a central pivot can be used to set out curved work. Cant bays are set out from a framed timber profile.

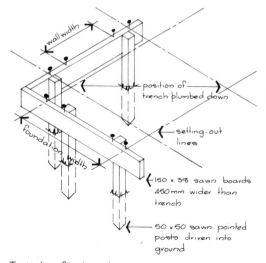

Typical profile boards

Foundation trench level pegs are usually established individually by means of an optical level from the established datum. Another method is to set up sight rails at the ends of each trench and fix intermediate levels by means of boning rods.

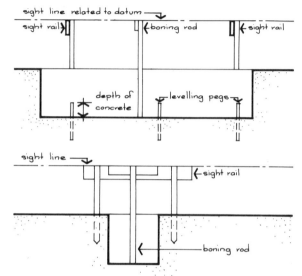

Levelling in foundation bottom using sight rails and boning rods

A third method is to use a straight edge and spirit level to set in a series of pegs from one whose level has previously been accurately set.

8.06

The accuracy of setting out and levelling in the excavations cannot be too highly stressed. On this initial work will depend much of the final accuracy of the building. With framed building, accuracy must be absolutely precise as steelwork is prepared to such fine tolerances as to allow no latitude for inaccurate setting out on site.

9.00 Site preparation and plant

The Building Regulations (C2 Preparation of site*) require that site areas shall be cleared of all turf and vegetable matter and, if necessary due to damp conditions, the fall or location of the site, the sub-soil must be drained or steps taken to protect the building from damage from moisture. Any existing site drains must be kept in proper operation if cut or disturbed during the course of the works.

The site area mentioned above is defined in the regulations (A2)* as the area actually covered by the building and its foundations. The depth of excavation to remove turf and vegetable matter is not specified.

9.01

The removal of turf and vegetable matter is required for two reasons:

(i) Such material if left under the building would generally die off and on rotting down become compressed by the load imposed on it by the floors and allow settlement and possible failure of the slabs.

(ii) Incorporated in the top soil are numerous plants and growths which could continue to grow under the building causing uplift of the floor slab and possible failure.

Although no depth is stipulated for the removal of turf and top soil, the precise depth of the latter will be established from trial holes or borings and can therefore be specified with some accuracy. Otherwise a generally accepted minimum of 150 mm of turf and top soil is removed. This top soil may be removed from site when it will generally command a good price or it may be deposited in spoil heaps on site for future re-use in the preparation of landscaping around the building. The decision for removal or retention will depend on a number of factors, not least of which will be the area of free site available and the location and siting of site huts and storage required for the works.

9.02

One of the prime requirements of the site is a continuous supply of clean, pure water. If possible this should be obtained from the local water authority main through either a permanent connection or the installation of a standpipe. Where main water is not available, local river, or well water must be tested to comply with BS 3148. Temporary plumbing is usually installed to bring water from source to point of use which is often stored in galvanised cisterns. These must not be used for washing tools or fouling of the water supply will ensue.

9.03

Legislation, the needs of efficient management and most building contracts require that contractors provide temporary accommodation on building sites for a variety of purposes. This can be summarised as follows:

(i) Huts to accommodate the management staff, i.e. foreman, site manager or surveyor, providing in addition for the storage of drawings and papers.

(ii) Similar accommodation for the use of the Clerk of Works and occasional use by the inspecting architect.

(iii) Welfare accommodation for the workmen which can include messing and canteen facilities, provision for the storage and drying of clothing.

(iv) Latrines for the use of site staff.

(v) Storage sheds for safe and weatherproof storage of valuable material for the use of the works or material that would deteriorate quickly if exposed to the weather.

(vi) Proper bins and hard standing for the storage of ballast, timber, bricks and roofing tiles.

The layout of this accommodation will suit each particular site but in the main the huts of supervisory and management staff are placed at the site entrance to control access to the site and supervise the movement of materials.

9.04

In some areas, the problem of pilfering materials and vandalism is serious. Security is essential and sites are often completely enclosed with high wire security fences provided with heavy lockable gates. These compounds are sometimes provided with high close-boarded fences where the site frontage is either short or directly impinging on well used footways in city streets.

9.05

With the high cost of labour, mechanisation has taken over much of the heavy work once carried out by building labourers. Although the capital outlay is high, increased output is considered to be worth the initial expenditure. Plant in general use on most small and medium sized sites includes the following:

(i) Pneumatic tyred or caterpillar tracked excavators incorporating front hydraulic blades or shovels for site stripping and loading excavated material into trucks for carting away from site.

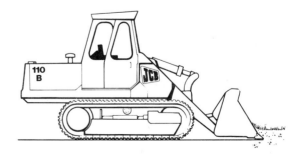

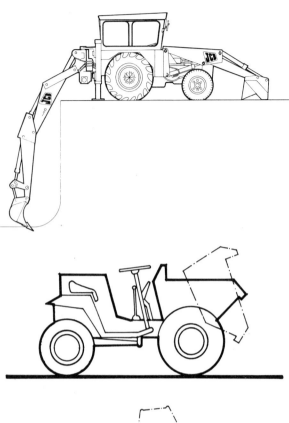

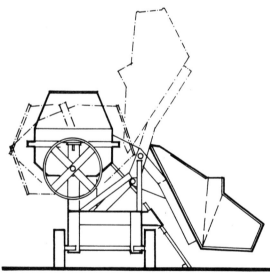

(ii) Similar machines with hydraulic operated back acter arms incorporating digging shovels of various widths for trench and foundation excavations up to depths of 6 m.

(iii) Small motorised dumper trucks with capacities of about 1 cubic metre for moving small quantities of excavated material, concrete and other materials about the site

(iv) Small motorised hoists suitable for use on buildings from three floors in height upwards to raise small quantities of materials and barrows from ground level to the scaffolding stages.

(v) Small motorised mixers to produce mortar for bricklaying and small quantities of concrete as required. Some sites still find it more economical to make all their own concrete but in some cases this is produced in central batch mixing plants and brought to site in revolving drums constructed onto specially designed trucks.

(vi) Small items of tools and plant such as barrows, hods for lifting bricks and roofing tiles, shovels, picks and crowbars, banker boards and buckets, etc.

(vii) Scaffolding including tubular supports, patent couplings and timber scaffold boards, required for all wet work about 1.5 m in height. Included are moveable platforms for interior work and isolated tower scaffolds for particular and restricted situations. (17.00 *et seq.*)

9.06

Larger sites may require more sophisticated plant to deal with larger quantities and weights of materials , often raised to far greater heights. Tower cranes may be used for handling concrete in large skips and large precast construction units. Sophisticated pumping equipment may be installed to pump concrete or plaster to the site of works. Hoists of large capacity may be needed with sophisticated controls to take workmen to upper floors of high blocks. Complicated pumping equipment may be needed to keep deep excavations free from ground water.

Module C Building Elements, Practice and Materials

10.00 Constituent parts and building elements
All buildings are composed of a number of constituent parts which perform various functions and make different contributions to the health, safety and welfare of the occupants. The number and division of these vary little with any but specialised buildings and may be summarised as follows:

(i) *The substructure* which comprises all foundation and oversite work up to the level of the damp proof course. The design of the foundations depends on a variety of factors, all or some of which may be pertinent. These include the type and bearing value of the subsoil, the loading of the building, the spacing of isolated parts of support, the presence of ground water, the slope of the ground, the availability of particular materials and the design and materials used in the overlying structure.

(ii) *The superstructure* comprising:

(a) the walls needed to protect the occupants from the weather, to provide insulation from external heat, cold and noise, and provide security for the occupants and contents.

(b) floors to provide level areas for support and working surfaces, fire and sound resistance

(c) roofs which provide enclosure from the weather, insulation from heat and cold and security for occupants and contents from fire in adjoining buildings.

10.01
In addition to the constituent parts of the building, each contains a number of additional elements which provide for the comfort of the occupants and assist in its proper functioning. These can be divided into primary and secondary elements, primary elements being mainly concerned with the structural envelope and secondary with internal fittings and finishes and non-structural items.

10.02
Primary elements including the following:

(i) windows to provide natural daylighting and ventilation necessary for human health and wellbeing.

(ii) doors and frames for human and vehicular access to the building and human escape in cases of fire or explosion.

(iii) chimneys and flues for the removal of fumes and products of combustion.

10.03
Secondary elements include the following:

(i) internal partitions including non-loadbearing internal partitions of brick and blockwork, timber studding etc, dividing the interior to suit the needs of the occupants.

(ii) internal doors with their linings and architraves, to provide privacy and security and in certain circumstances to provide resistance against the spread of fire or smoke.

(iii) skirtings to protect the base of the internal partitions from floor cleaning damage and to provide a stop for wall finishes.

(iv) applied finishes on walls, ceilings and floors to ensure hygiene and provide a decorative effect for the interior of the building.

10.04
Mention has been made of finishes when describing the surface of internal and external walls, floors, ceilings and other elements. Finishes to some building materials are required for a number of reasons:

(i) to seal the surface against the penetration of water or deleterious substances with which it might come into contact. Penetration might cause rotting of the fibres, in the case or wood, or the promotion of fungal growth and decomposition of the plaster on brick faced external solid walls.

(ii) to provide a surface which can be easily cleaned and kept free from dirt and bacteria. This is a requirement for medical operating theatres or kitchens where walls are often tiled to make cleaning easy and effective.

(iii) to provide a decorative effect or 'mood' in the particular room.

10.05
Two separate types of finish are in general use:

(i) *self-finishes* in which the finish is applied or formed during the preparation or manufacture of the material used. Examples include fair faced exposed brick and decorative blockwork, stone or marble, and

(ii) *applied finishes* in which the finish is applied after the supporting structure has been erected. Examples are plaster on brick or block walls, painting onto plaster or wood, panelling or dry lining applied to walls, floor finishes and floor screeds.

11.00 Factors affecting the choice and fundamentals of construction and materials
A building site is, in reality, a temporary factory, operating for much of its time in the open air and carrying out a number of functions which are closely allied and directly related to the functions of its more comfortably enclosed industrial counterpart. Materials are ordered and delivery is taken of specified raw materials and components. Labour is provided by men generally skilled in basic building crafts — carpenters, bricklayers, plumbers etc — plus supervisory and managerial staff at lower and intermediate levels. Assisted by the usual mechanical and hand-operated tools and plant, the building is assembled.

11.01
In addition to the building site, associated production centres are active in supplying manufactured materials and components for incorporation in the building. Some of these provide basic materials such as bricks, cement, tiles; some centres themselves fabricate and assemble manufactured materials into components such as metal windows, sanitary fittings, structural steelwork. Joinery manufacturers take sawn timber and prepare and fabricate joinery, doors and windows for the works. All these form, with numerous builder's merchants, sand and ballast quarries and specialist contractors for electrical and heating installations, an industry of great size and complexity.

11.02
The selection of a particular method of construction will depend on the consideration of a number of factors, taking into account a great deal of information gleaned from the building client's brief, the knowledge of site conditions, the restraints of planning and building control, the known limitations of possible building materials and the experience and competence of local builders.

11.03
Cost will enter into matters at an early stage in the proceedings. Money (or the lack of it) is a basic raw material of the building industry, required not only for financing the purchase of the site, the employment of professional staff for the preparation of design and production drawings and their attendant specifications and bills of quantities but also for financing the commencement of the work and its continuity by periodic payments as the work proceeds.

11.04
There is, therefore, a close relationship between the requirements of the building owner or client illustrated in terms of the architect's agreed design, the amount of finance available to realise this and the constructional alternatives which may be employed.

11.05
The basic alternatives available for the construction of small domestic buildings and single storey factory or warehouse projects are as follows:

SMALL DOMESTIC STRUCTURES OF TWO OR THREE STORIES

(a) Brick traditional building employing cavity walls on concrete foundations under a sloping tile-finished roof with internal walls of lightweight blocks and floors of timber board and joist constructions.

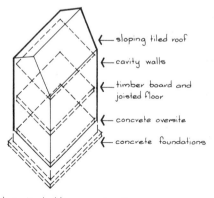

Typical domestic building construction

(b) Brick cross wall construction comprising load bearing compartmenting walls at intervals, the external enclosure being effected by prefabricated wall and window panels, usually of wood and incorporating roofs and floors similar to (a). In certain circumstances where fire resistance to intermediate floors required under the Building Regulations needs to be greater than that provided by timber construction, reinforced concrete floors can be incorporated.

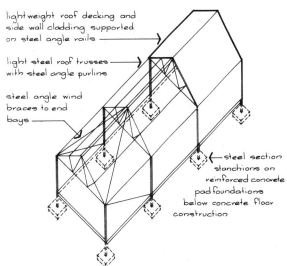

lightweight roof decking and side wall cladding supported on steel angle rails

light steel roof trusses with steel angle purlins

steel angle wind braces to end bays

steel section stanchions on reinforced concrete pad foundations below concrete floor construction

Typical steel-framed single storey factory or warehouse construction (single bay)

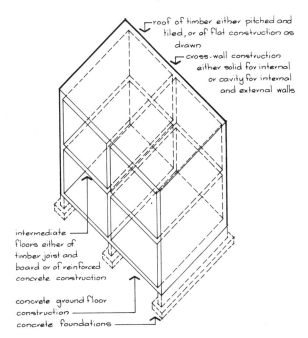

roof of timber either pitched and tiled, or of flat construction as drawn

cross-wall construction either solid for internal or cavity for internal and external walls

intermediate floors either of timber joist and board or of reinforced concrete construction

concrete ground floor construction

concrete foundations

Typical domestic terrace cross-wall construction

SINGLE-STOREY FACTORY OR WAREHOUSE
(c) Framed construction comprising steel stanchions or reinforced concrete columns supported on isolated concrete pad foundation and carrying roof framing of steel or concrete designed to support light weight roof decking. In addition larger structures are usually formed from a framework of steel or concrete, designed to withstand not only high loadings from the weight of the structure but also pressure from high winds acting on the enclosing envelope.

MULTI-STOREY FRAMED PROJECTS
(d) A construction in which columns and beams are connected together to form a rigid framework to which is added reinforced concrete floors and roofs and walls either of prefabricated panels or metal framing with glass infill or reinforced concrete.

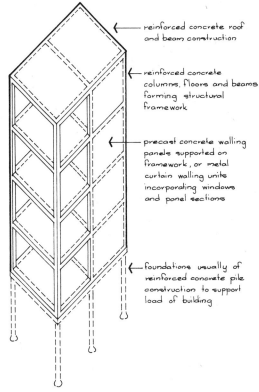

reinforced concrete roof and beam construction

reinforced concrete columns, floors and beams forming structural framework

precast concrete walling panels supported on framework, or metal curtain walling units incorporating windows and panel sections

foundations usually of reinforced concrete pile construction to support load of building

Typical multi-storey framed building construction

11.06
From this it will be seen that most building structures depend on a relatively small number of basic building materials for their construction. These are briefly as follows:

(i) *Sand and ballast* used as aggregates for mortar (sand) and concrete (fine and coarse aggregate). In most cases these occur naturally in beds from which they are recovered either by mechanical digger or by dredging where the deposits occur in water. Washing is usually necessary to remove loam, organic material or salt (where dredging is from tidal estuaries) and the material is graded to the various sizes required for particular grades of concrete. In some areas naturally occurring sand and ballast is unobtainable or costly. Often, however, locally produced stone is more than satisfactory providing that it is crushed and graded to the required sizes. (See BS 882: 1965 *Aggregates from natural sources for concrete*).

(ii) *Cement* for most contracts will be Portland of British manufacture which is delivered to site either in the manufacturer's sealed paper bags each containing 50 kg or loose in bulk delivery tankers from which it is pumped into large storage silos provided on site. Damp is the chief enemy of cement and it must be properly stored and used quickly or it will deteriorate rapidly. (See BS 12: 1958/Pt. 2. 1971 *Metric units – Portland cement*).

(iii) *Bricks* are the most popular material for walling especially for facing work, usually made to a standard size of 215 x 102.5 x 65 mm thick. Clay and shale bricks are made by weathering and breaking up the clay to provide a uniform mix of standard plasticity which is either moulded by hand or machine into uniformly sized blocks. These are then either stacked into a chamber in a Hoffman continuous kiln or passed through a continuous tunnel kiln where by raising the temperature to about $900°C$ the brick is fired to a uniform hard burnt unit. Hand made bricks are usually fired in an intermittent Scotch kiln.

Three main types of brick are used in building:

(a) *Facing bricks* chosen for their colour and texture, either machine or hand-made from moulds and usually of clay. Colour varies from mixed multi reds/blues to grey and yellow according to the type of clay used and the method of firing. Of low strength they are also relatively costly.

(b) *Common bricks* either of clay or shale of standard size produced either with a smooth face or grooved to provide a key for plastering. They are used where appearance is not important, to be finished with plaster or a similar covering and where strength is relatively important.

(c) *Engineering bricks* produced by means of hydraulic presses either by moulding or extrusion and generally of clay or shale. Colour is either red or blue, the appearance is greasy and bricks of standard sizes are produced in two strengths:

Class A – 69.0 (Average compression strength
Class B – 48.5 in MN/m^2.)

Class B. is in general use for foundations and manholes. (See BS 3921: 1974 *Clay bricks*)

(iv) In addition, calcium silicate bricks are produced made from lime and sand (or crushed flint) moulded under pressure and subjected to steam pressure in an oven or autoclave. By adjusting the pressures, bricks can be produced providing minimum compressive strengths from $7/48.5$ mN/m^2, thus producing bricks suitable for all work from common brickwork to foundations (See BS 187 Pt. 2: 1970 *Sand lime bricks*)

(v) *Blocks*, especially those manufactured from light weight aggregates or incorporating entrained air in their composition have a reasonable compressive strength suitable for use in domestic two storey construction and, having a low thermal conductivity, increase the thermal insulation of a building when used in conjunction with brick as the external leaf in cavity walling. Usually produced to a size of 450 x 225 mm with thicknesses of 50, 75, 100 and 150 mm, blocks are also used in quantities for low strength partitions and non-loadbearing walls where dead weight is a serious problem. (See CP 122: 1952 *Walls and partitions of blocks and slabs*).

(vi) *Steel* for building is either produced as rods or welded wire mesh for reinforcing concrete or in the form of rolled sections for structural steelwork from mild or high tensile steel ingots. Both the composition of the weld, the diameter of the rods and the profiles of the sections are carefully controlled and must conform to the appropriate standards. (See BS 4 Pt. 1. 1972 *Hot rolled steel sections*. Pt. 2. 1969 *Hot rolled hollow steel sections*. BS 4449: 1969 *Hot rolled steel bars for reinforced concrete*. BS 4483: 1969 *Steel fabric for the reinforcement of concrete*).

(vii) *Timber* for most building purposes is imported softwood, generally of the pine species. The timber is delivered in sections which have been sawn to a range of sizes in general use in the building industry and in a series of preferred metric lengths (metres):

1.80	2.10	3.00	4.20	5.10	6.00
	2.40	3.30	4.50	5.40	6.30
	2.70	3.60	4.80	5.70	
		3.90			

Not all sizes can be obtained in these lengths, usually from 75 x 38 mm upwards. The timber needs to be squared and thicknessed by a wood machinist using a planer/thicknesser after air or kiln seasoning before it is suitable for joinery. In addition, it is also often imperative for structural timbers to be impregnated against attack by certain timber borers (Building Regulations B3 and B4*) especially in certain designated areas. Impregnation carried out in accordance with the appropriate British Standard is obligatory and, because of the continued spread of this problem, it is suggested that all structural timbers be so treated. (See BS 4072: 1974 *Wood preservation by water borne compositions*).

A number of other requirements are obligatory under the Building Regulations (D14)*. The design of timber structures includes for the use of stress graded timber and Schedule 6* which gives 'deemed to satisfy' sizes of timber for various spans, centres and loadings implies the use of stress graded material. Two grades are noted, GSI (General structural grade) and SS (Special structural grade) for both visual and machine graded timbers. (See CP 112 *The use of structural timber;* BS 4978: 1973 *Timber grades for structural use;* Technical Note No. 25: *Stress grading of timber* – Forest Products Research Laboratory).

Module D The Substructure of Building

12.00 Substructures – primary function and constituent parts

Building Regulations D4-7* (Deemed to satisfy provisions)
CP 110 Pts. 1, 2 and 3: 1972, *or*
CP 114 Pt. 2: 1969

12.01

All building structures incorporate two independent forces:

(a) The dead load which comprises the actual gross weight of the structure, and

(b) The live load which is provided by the weight of installed furniture and loose equipment and of the human occupants calculated on the empirical basis of a given number of kilos/m² of net floor area as laid down in the appropriate Code of Practice for the type of occupation, i.e.

1½ kN/m² for domestic properties
    up to two stories in height;
4 kN/m² for commercial properties
    (see CP3, Chapter 5)

12.02

These forces are transmitted throughout the structure, finally being applied onto the surface of the ground on which the building stands. In many cases the loads being applied are neither evenly distributed across the whole surface in contact with the ground or concentric to the centreline of the particular feature of the structure, i.e. the foundation wall or the base of a pier or column in a framed structure. The effect of these uneven and unequal loads will be for the weight to compress the soil under the building structure in varying degrees, causing unequal stresses in the overlying building which will show as cracking.

12.03

A further problem to be resolved is the unequal composition of soil under a building. Overlying most building sites is a layer of vegetable soil, usually about 150 mm thick. Under this is a strata generally called subsoil which may be formed from either the decomposition or erosion of rocks or from the deposition

of water borne particles. Underlying the subsoil at varying depths there may be found rock, which in a similar way to subsoil will enjoy varying degrees of compressive strength sometimes depending on the quality of ground water present in its composition. Both topsoil and subsoil will contain in varying degrees plant and vegetable growth which, as growing organisms, can continue to grow and expand under a building causing eventual disturbance to the overlying fabric.

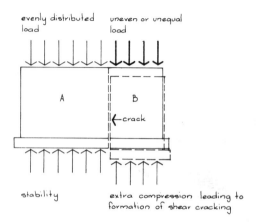

Formation of settlement cracking due to unequal stressing or loading of a structure

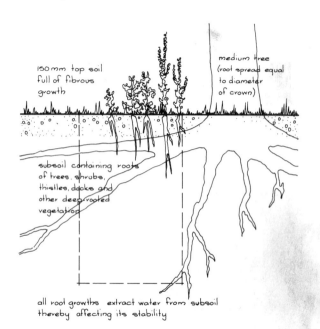

all root growths extract water from subsoil thereby affecting its stability

12.04

Many sites, especially in urban areas, are prepared by demolition of former structures or filling in to a new level with rubbish or previously excavated material from another site. Unless the filling has been properly compacted throughout or has been in position for a great many years it is unlikely that it will be of sufficient strength to carry a new building unless the loading is very light or is spread evenly over the whole area of the building.

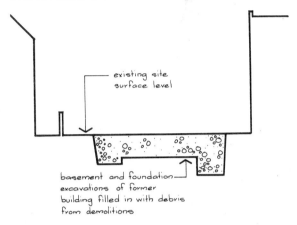

existing site surface level

basement and foundation excavations of former building filled in with debris from demolitions

12.05

Soils and rocks are composed of natural materials, chemical compounds which can cause reactions especially in the presence of water. As water penetrating the subsoil is often acidic, these chemical reactions can be a problem in building construction. This is especially so with the presence of soluble sulphates in certain clay subsoils which attack the cement content in foundations causing this to disintegrate. Care must be taken to determined the presence of these soluble sulphates and ensure that the foundations incorporate cement which is specially formulated to resist this attack.

12.06

Lastly soil containing quantities of water is affected by the temperature and humidity of the climate. Excess rainfall can cause excess water content of the subsoil with subsequent swelling or heaving of the surface. This is a common problem in clay. It follows that, in this instance, a period of drought or drying winds will extract water from the clay causing it to shrink causing serious surface cracking. Certain granular subsoils such as sand or gravel and soft rocks such as chalk, when used for filling, can freeze in cold weather to some depth. This causes the material to expand and again can cause heaving of the surface level, disrupting building structures.

12.07

Foundations must therefore be designed to withstand all these different problems, whether produced by the design of the overlying building structure or by the subsoil of the site on which the building is to be erected. To this effect foundations should comply with the following criteria:

(i) Foundations should be capable of transmitting to the ground the combined dead and live loads (plus any wind loads imposed) without any significant settlement or differential movement of any part of the building structure or adjoining works or buildings.

(ii) Foundations should be constructed at a sufficient depth to avoid movement by the swelling, shrinkage or freezing of the subsoil.

(iii) Foundation concrete mixes must be formulated so as to resist attack by chemicals such as soluble sulphates normally found in certain subsoils.

12.08

To meet the requirements of these criteria, the Building Regulations (D4-7)* have laid down certain design features which will generally cause foundations to be constructed which will not fail in these circumstances. These may be summarised as follows for simple strip concrete foundations suitable for domestic two storey buildings (D7):

(i) The foundation constructed of plain unreinforced concrete is to be placed centrally under the wall.

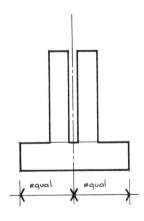

equal   equal

(ii) Wide variation in subsoil or made ground is not permitted under the foundation.

(iii) The width of the foundation to be dependant on the total load and the type of soil.

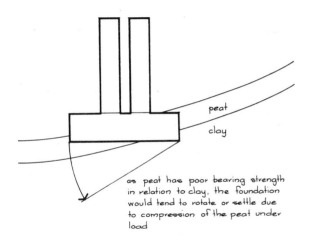

as peat has poor bearing strength in relation to clay, the foundation would tend to rotate or settle due to compression of the peat under load

(v) Where the levels of the site dictate a change in level of the foundation bottom the concrete must overlap not less than 300 mm and not less than the thickness of the foundation concrete.

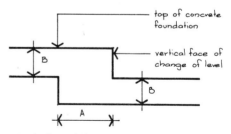

top of concrete foundation

vertical face of change of level

A is to be not less than B and a minimum of 300 mm

(iv) Concrete shall be composed of a mix comprising 50 kg. cement: 0.1m³ fine aggregate (to pass mesh 4.75 mm square, 10% to pass 0.5 mm mesh): 0.2m³ coarse aggregate (retained on 4.75 mm square mesh of maximum size 38 mm); all to BS 882:1965.

(vi) The minimum thickness of the foundation is to be as follows:

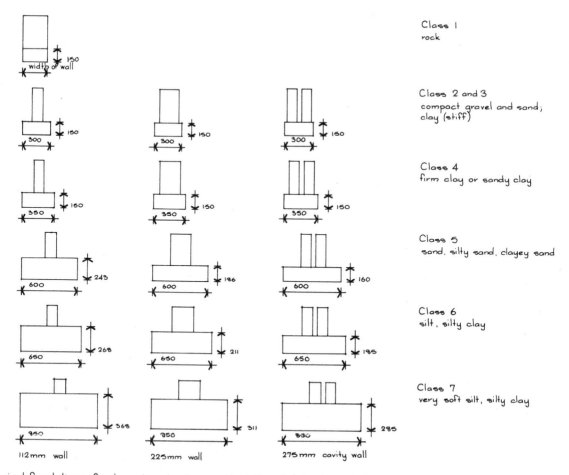

Class 1
rock

Class 2 and 3
compact gravel and sand;
clay (stiff)

Class 4
firm clay or sandy clay

Class 5
sand, silty sand, clayey sand

Class 6
silt, silty clay

Class 7
very soft silt, silty clay

112mm wall   225mm wall   275mm cavity wall

Typical foundations for domestic structures with differential loadings between 20 and 30 N/m

(vii) Piers, buttresses or chimneys projecting from the wall must have the foundation projection carried round their base.

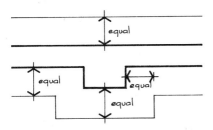

In practice, in most soils, calculations are not required for walls to domestic two-storey structures where the loading does not exceed 30 kN/m. run of wall so long as the thickness of the concrete and its projection is at least 150 mm. To avoid expansion or contraction of subsoils due to excessive rain or drought or prolonged cold weather, foundations should generally be placed at least 900 mm below the finished level of the surrounding site.

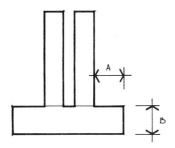

thickness of concrete (B) not less than 150 mm, and not less than projection from wall (A)
minimum projection of a foundation (A) is therefore 150 mm

13.00 Foundations — brick walls and partitions

Most excavations for foundations are carried out in a fairly loose, often granular material, with little cohesion and a tendency to fall into the excavation if left for any period of time. With relatively shallow trenches this problem is rarely more than a temporary inconvenience but in excavations over 1 m in depth some support to the sides is necessary.

(i) to protect from injury or possible death any men working in the trench, and

(ii) to ensure that any material or work is protected from damage due to the collapse of the excavation sides.

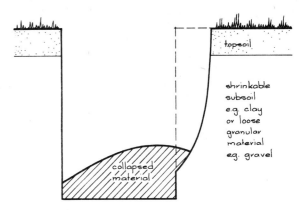

Typical collapse of trench wall in non-cohesive or granular subsoil

13.01
The possibility of side wall collapse is directly related to the natural angle of repose of the subsoil, i.e. the maximum angle at which the material is stable, as follows:

Rock and chalk 80/90°
Gravel soil   45°
Sandy soil   35°
Silt and clay   25/30°

13.02
In shallow trenches in granular or non-cohesive soils (gravel, sand or silt) simple strutting of the sides of the excavation is generally sufficient to ensure stability of the trench walls.

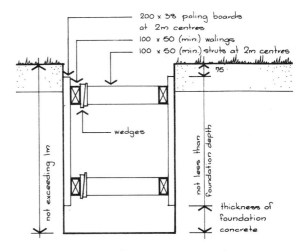

Typical trench timbering in cohesive soils, excavations not exceeding 1m depth
note: in dry, loose soils the poling boards are replaced by continuous horizontal close boarding from trench bottom to surface

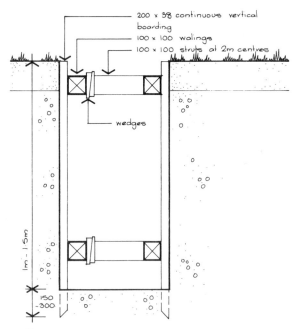

200 x 38 continuous vertical boarding
100 x 100 walings
100 x 100 struts at 2m centres

wedges

1m - 1·5m

150 -300

Typical timbering in dry, loose soils, excavations not exceeding 1·5m depth
note : in wet loose soils, the walings may need wedge driven next to boarding to maintain support as water drains out of subsoil and is pumped from trench

13.03

In deeper excavations it may be necessary to adapt both the strutting and the size of the trench:

(a) to allow men to work at depth — the trench must be wide enough for free movement in digging, and

(b) to allow excavated material to be cast out of the trench — temporary boarded areas may be necessary from which earth thrown out of the lower excavation can be removed and cast onto the ground well clear of the side of the trench.

13.04

Occasionally large square excavations are required of some depth in granular or non-cohesive soils. Here it is often difficult to shutter and strut the sides to protect the works and in this instance a method of excavation known as the 'dumpling method' is employed. The foundation trench to the wall is excavated leaving an 'island' of soil in the middle which is used as an abutment to one side of the boarding and strutting. The foundation is cast and the walls erected, the brickwork being built around the struts which are left in position. When the wall is complete and the strutting and boarding is stripped

out, the holes made good, the central island of sub-soil is excavated and the gap around the perimeter backfilled in the normal manner.

13.05

Where the subsoil is relatively stable but still requires some support to protect men and works, timber raking shores supporting timber polings can be employed. These are, however, obstructive and if the works are of any size, sheet steel piling may be employed to advantage despite the heavy equipment necessary to drive it into the ground.

13.06

All excavations make water in wet weather, water draining into them from the surrounding site. Water from all sources must be controlled in site excavations either,

(a) by digging sumps which are emptied by hand or mechanical pumps, or

(b) by natural drainage if the slope of the site and natural ditches permit.

13.07

The bottoms of all excavations must be dry and free from mud before concreting. Traffic over waterlogged soil will result in the formation of thick mud which will have to be scraped out and the excavation 'bottomed up' by hand before being acceptable.

13.08

As soon as excavations are complete and the bottom surface approved, concreting must commence. Concrete for strip foundations must be laid level and to the required thickness,

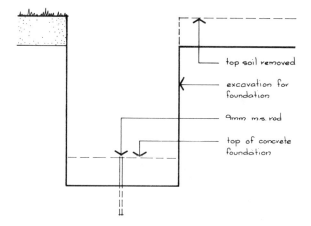

top soil removed

excavation for foundation

9mm m.s. rod

top of concrete foundation

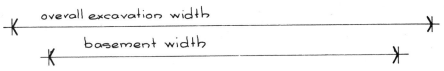

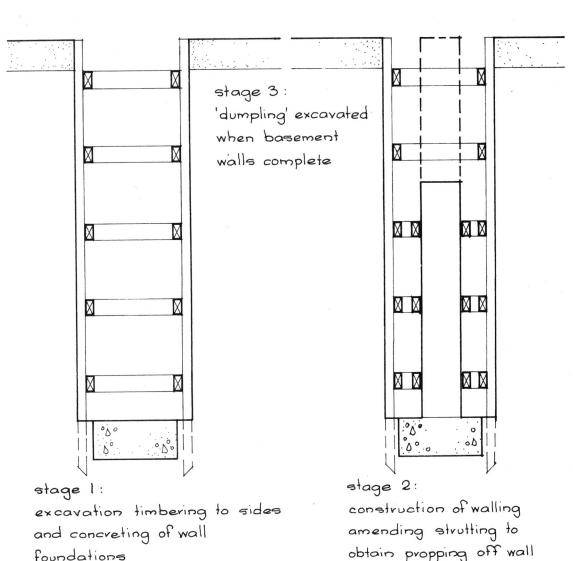

overall excavation width

basement width

stage 3:
'dumpling' excavated
when basement
walls complete

stage 1:
excavation timbering to sides
and concreting of wall
foundations

stage 2:
construction of walling
amending strutting to
obtain propping off wall

Excavation of basement and deep pad foundations in granular or non-cohesive soils

(i) to provide a level bed for the construction of the overlying walls, and

(ii) to meet both the regulations and the need for sufficient strength and stability.

Both these conditions are met by placing 9 mm steel pins in the bottom of the trench, protruding the full depth of the concrete and with their tops level with the required upper surface. The pins are concreted in.

13.09

The brick external walls are then constructed, usually in engineering quality bricks set in cement mortar up to the level of the damp proof course (C7)*. To prevent damage to the wall during backfilling of excavated material or hardcore which now takes place the cavity is filled with fine weak mix concrete up to 150 mm below the damp proof course. To allow any water which gains entry to the cavity to find its way quickly to the outside, vertical joints (perpends) in the brickwork above the top of the cavity filling are left open every third joint. Trenches are backfilled in consolidated layers not exceeding 225 mm using hardcore under the internal floors and selected excavated material externally.

13.10

The construction of foundation walls up to damp proof course level for both floors of solid and suspended timber construction can be constructed for domestic type buildings up to two stories in height in accordance with the sketches.

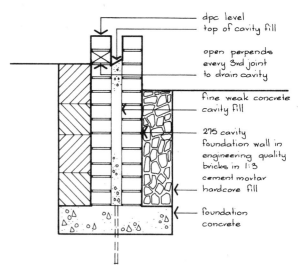

Typical foundation works for domestic buildings employing strip concrete foundations and brick cavity walls

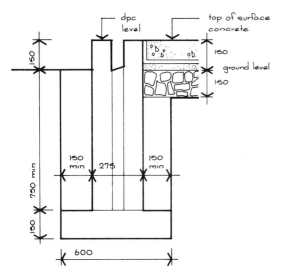

Typical foundation for domestic building up to two storeys in height with solid ground floor in reasonable subsoil

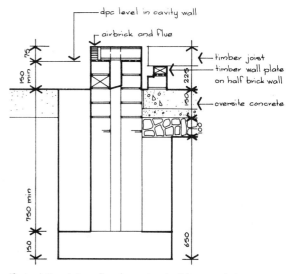

Typical foundation for domestic building up to two storeys in height with timber suspended ground floor in reasonable subsoils

These suggestions are suitable for reasonable subsoils in Classes II, III, IV and V of Building Regulation D7*.

13.11

Where site conditions, or superstructure varies or economic factors differ, alternative forms of construction can be considered.

(a) In very wet, marsh ground where the subsoil has little bearing strength (D7 Class VII) it may be advis-

able to consider the use of a reinforced concrete raft. This comprises a bed of concrete, reinforced with mild steel rods or mesh reinforcement, provided with downstand edge beams to increase resistance to hardcore and subsoil squeezing out from under the slab when this is loaded by the addition of the superstructure.

(b) An alternative foundation for subsoils of little bearing strength can be provided by drilling short holes of 400 or 450 mm dia, into the ground and

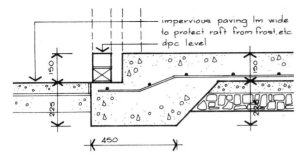

Typical reinforced concrete raft construction

impervious paving 1m wide to protect raft from frost, etc.
dpc level

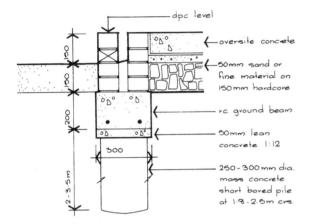

dpc level
oversite concrete
50mm sand or fine material on 150mm hardcore
rc. ground beam
50mm lean concrete 1:12
250-300mm dia. mass concrete short bored pile at 1.8-2.5m crs.

Typical short bored pile and ground beam foundation for domestic building up to three storeys in height

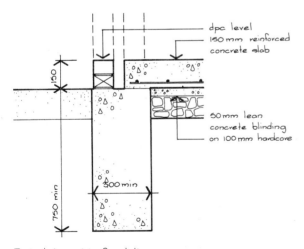

dpc level
150mm reinforced concrete slab
50mm lean concrete blinding on 100mm hardcore

Typical deep strip foundation

filling these with concrete. These constructions are known as short bored piles and their tops are connected with reinforced concrete beams on which the walls are constructed.

(c) Deep strip foundations may be considered where the design width of the concrete foundation is too narrow to permit men to lay bricks in the depth of the trench.

(d) Wide strip foundations, generally reinforced with mild steel rods or fabric reinforcement top and bottom, to withstand the pressure of a relatively thin highly loaded wall when the subsoil has a low bearing strength.

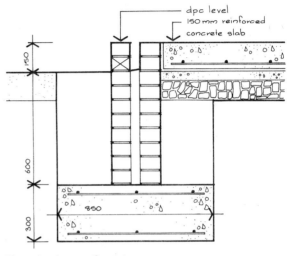

dpc level
150mm reinforced concrete slab

Typical wide strip foundation

13.12

Foundations should be provided under loadbearing partitions in a similar manner to external walls. It is not generally necessary for the concrete to be carried down to the same depth, as the subsoil under the building is protected from the elements and will not move through shrinkage or frost action during the life of the building. Care must, however, be taken to ensure that the subsoil is satisfactory in the same manner as the external walls. So long as the foundation concrete is carried down into the subsoil this will generally be sufficient.

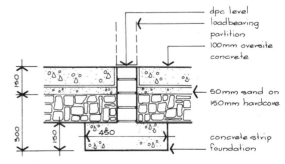

dpc level
loadbearing partition
100mm oversite concrete
50mm sand on 150mm hardcore
concrete strip foundation

Typical foundation for loadbearing 112mm brick or 100mm block partition for two storey domestic building

13.13

Where non-loadbearing partitions are provided it is generally sufficient to thicken out the oversite concrete to a thickness of from 150/225 mm to carry the extra dead load imposed by the partition.

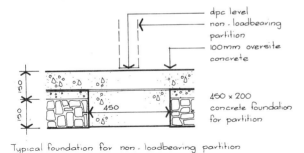

Typical foundation for non-loadbearing partition

14.00 Foundations — steel columns and isolated piers

Isolated point loads provided by steel columns or brick piers follow the general rules of foundations in respect of:

(a) Loading of subsoil.

(b) Depth to counteract climatic conditions.

14.01

In most cases the foundation is calculated to provide a square foundation of a thickness to withstand the load placed upon it which will tend to produce pressures which will endeavour to punch a hole through the concrete (punching shear). To counteract this tendency the concrete may be strengthened with mild steel rod or fabric reinforcement which will also assist in preventing the foundation pad, if large, from a tendency to fracture or fold up under the load.

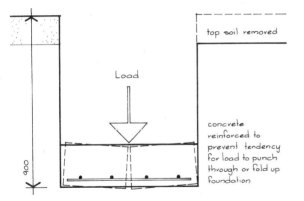

14.02

Steel stanchions are provided with base plates to spread the load and these must be secured down to the concrete foundations with bolts fitted with plates under the head to provide resistance to upward pull. Mortices are formed in the foundation concrete either by

(i) formation of the hole by casting in a sleeve of expanded metal lath, or

(ii) by inserting a polystyrene plug which is burnt out after the concrete hardens.

14.03

The baseplate of the stanchion is wedged up with steel shims (tapered wedges) to the correct level and the bolts are grouted into the holes provided, the gap between the steel baseplate and the concrete being packed solid with cement and sand mortar (1:1) or run with neat cement grout.

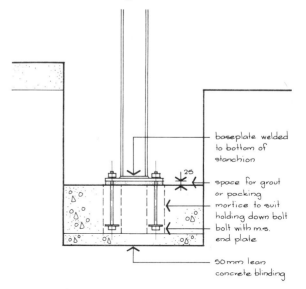

14.04

Brick piers are often constructed directly off the concrete foundation, generally in engineering bricks in cement mortar. The base of the pier is often provided with offset courses to spread the load more evenly over the top surface of the concrete.

15.00 Resistance to rising damp

Foundations cannot be considered in isolation, their design and construction depends on other factors, especially the construction of the ground floor. These factors may be summarised as follows:

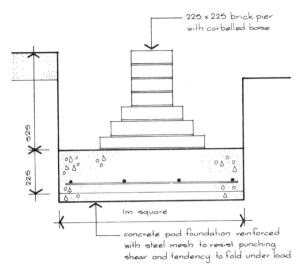

225 x 225 brick pier
with corbelled base

525
225
1m square

concrete pad foundation reinforced
with steel mesh to resist punching
shear and tendency to fold under load

Typical isolated foundation to carry brick pier or steel stanchion

(i) The method and materials used in the construction of the external envelope of the building.

(ii) The construction of the ground floor — whether solid concrete with an integral finish or a suspended timber floor.

(iii) The method of preventing damp rising out of the ground and affecting both overlying structure and finished.

15.01

In structures faced with brick or blockwork, it is usual for the wall to be carried directly off the foundation concrete, varying the constituent materials from within the ground where conditions of continuous damp and likely chemical action are greater, to portions of the structure exposed to the atmosphere. In practice only foundation quality blocks and bricks are at all suitable for substructure works below dpc. Bricks, blocks and concrete are essentially cellular in structure and all can be penetrated in varying degrees by water and water vapour. In addition all floors next to or in contact with the ground must comply with three conditions (C3 and C5)*

(i) They must be constructed as to prevent moisture from the ground reaching the upper surface and constituting a potential health hazard.

(ii) They must prevent any part of the floor from being affected by water or water vapour.

(iii) Any filling provided under the floor to provide a level or stable base on which to construct that floor must not contain any water soluble sulphates which may cause damage to the floor.

15.02

It is therefore essential to provide an efficient damp proof course to prevent rising damp or water vapour from passing into the building through the ground floor. As this damp proof course should extend through all walls rising out of the ground, for similar reasons, great care must be taken to ensure that this overall protection is continuous and unlikely to fail throughout the life of the building.

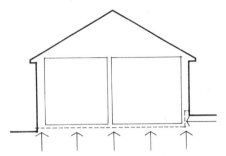

damp courses must be continuous to be effective, and composed of durable materials to last the expected life of the building

15.03

Filling to provide a level bed on which to provide a suitable ground floor base, should be of either stone or brick rubble, free from old plaster and mortar (which is likely to contain soluble sulphates), crushed or broken to pass a 75 mm mesh. This is placed in position and well rolled or consolidated with a mechanical vibrator to the required thickness which should not be less than 100 mm. The maximum thickness of hardcore in any one layer should not exceed 225 mm and filling of this thickness should be well watered in with a hose while consolidation takes place. Where filling exceeds 600 mm thick, consideration needs to be given either to a timber suspended floor or a suspended reinforced concrete slab.

15.04

The primary protection of the interior of the building from rising damp is provided by laying a bed of concrete not less than 100 mm thick over the whole area of the interior of the building. The composition of this concrete is identical to that for foundations except that the maximum size of coarse aggregate should not exceed 19 mm. The concrete is usually, in practice, laid over a layer of 1000 gauge polythene sheet to separate this from the underlying hardcore bed. Where the site is particularly wet or the floor finish will be of timber or some such material easily affected by damp, a horizontal damp proof membrane may be laid in addition over the surface of the over-site concrete. This membrane may comprise two or three coats of cold bitumen emulsion, carried up the side walls to meet the damp proof course provided in them and ultimately protected by an overlying cement and sand screeding coat.

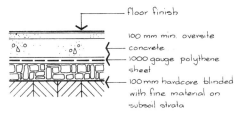

Minimum requirements for protection of interior from damp rising through floor

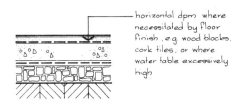

Additional damp proof membrane where specifically required

15.05

Where the concrete bed forms the base for an integral floor finish, such as plastic tiles, the level must be so contrived that the upper surface is not less than 150 mm above the highest level of external ground or pavings.

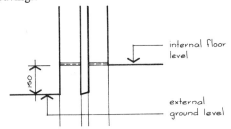

Where the concrete protects and supports a suspended timber floor the upper surface must not be lower than the highest level of the external ground or pavings.

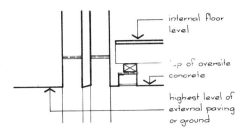

15.06

The prevention of rising damp in walls is provided by the insertion of a damp proof membrane. It is essential that the material selected complies with certain basic requirements:

(i) It is completely resistant to the passage of water and water vapour.

(ii) It is not affected by cement, lime or other materials with which it may come into contact.

(iii) Its life under normal usage will equal or exceed that of the building structure.

(iv) It will not fracture, tear or break under normal installed conditions.

15.07

The materials in general use for damp courses are either felt based bitumen or a polymer strip, produced in 10 m length rolls of widths to suit most wall or partition thicknesses, and bedded and pointed in cement mortar 1:3.

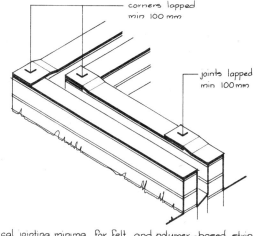

Typical jointing minima for felt and polymer-based strip damp courses

15.08

Other flexible damp courses used in special situations are lead (usually covered with bitumen to protect the metal from the corrosive effect of cement mortar on which it is bedded) and copper strip. Rigid materials used for damp proof courses include two courses of slate laid breaking joint or two courses of engineering bricks, both bedded and pointed in cement mortar (1:3).

15.09

It is essential that damp proof courses in walls and partitions are not only continuous but also placed so that they cannot be easily bridged. The level of the damp proof course in the external wall should be at least 150 mm above the level of the external ground or pavings and where timber wall plates are provided to support timber suspended ground floor construction a damp course must be provided immediately under the timber wall plate.

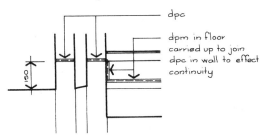

Typical dpc in external wall with solid ground floor construction

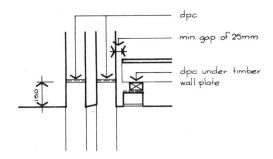

Typical dpc in external wall with suspended ground floor construction

In addition all partitions either penetrating the oversite concrete or bearing on it must also have a damp proof course.

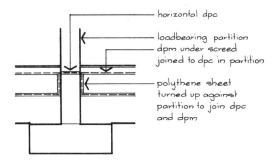

Dpc in typical loadbearing partition

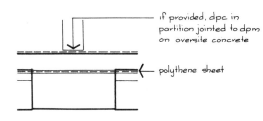

Dpc in typical non-loadbearing block partition

Care must be taken to ensure continuity between these damp courses and any provided in the oversite concrete itself (15.04).

Module E The Superstructure of Building

16.00 Superstructure – primary functions

The superstructure includes all those elements of the structure situated above but including the damp proof course. These elements generally comprise:

(i) The external envelope enclosing and protecting the interior, whether structural or not.

(ii) Internal walls and partitions, whether loadbearing or not.

(iii) Suspended floors.

(iv) The structural frame, if provided.

(v) The roof.

All elements can be constructed in a variety of ways and incorporate a number of differing materials. All, however, are required to perform certain duties and functions and the standards to which these must conform are clearly defined within the Building Regulations.

16.01 Structural stability

The whole of a building structure above the foundations must be so designed as to safely transmit the whole of the dead, imposed and wind loads without any deflection or deformation (D8)*.

'Dead load' is defined as the force due to the static mass of all permanent construction. The weight of materials is calculated in accordance with data provided in BS 648:1964 *Schedule of weights of building materials.*

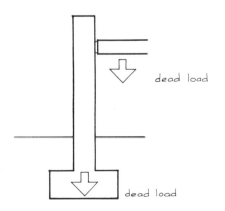

'Imposed load' is defined as the assumed loa produced by the intended use of the building including all distributed, concentrated, impac inertia and snow loads.

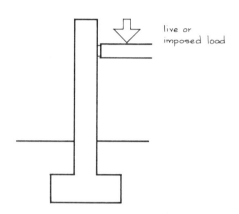

'Wind load' is defined as loads imposed by wind pressure or suction on the external surface of a building structure (D1)*.

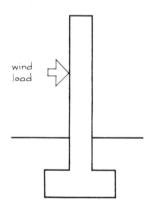

The calculation of all dead and imposed loads are carried out generally in accordance with CP3: Chapter V: Part 1:1967.

16.02 Fire resistance

All building materials and systems of construction have a degree of resistance to fire. This resistance can be measured by submitting a prepared unit to a measured exposure to fire, the degree of resistance being the length of time the sample survives the prescribed test defined without failure.

16.03
Generally the basic principles required of the elements forming the envelope of a building are as follows (E7/8/9)*:

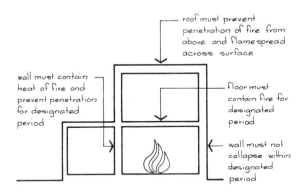

Walls should
(i) not collapse under fire.

(ii) not transmit heat enabling a fire to start on the opposite side.

(iii) not allow fire to penetrate to other buildings or areas within the same building.

Floors should
(i) be considered as including the ceiling finish below *and*

(ii) withstand the application of fire to the underside for a designated period of time without collapse (E9)*.

Roofs should
(i) not allow fire to penetrate the structure from above.

(ii) not allow flame to spread across the upper surface (E17)*.

16.04
There are, therefore, two requirements for building structures and materials:

(i) The ability to withstand fire and the passage of heat. This is known as the notional 'fire resistance' of a structure or material.

(ii) The ability to check the 'spread of flame' across the surface.

Both 'fire resistance' and 'spread of flame' are expressed as resistance for a period of time, the latter also requiring a maximum distance of flame travel within the specified period.

16.05
Minimum periods of fire resistance are required for all elements of structure as defined in the Building Regulations (E1)*. The period of fire resistance depends on the following:

(i) Overall height of the building — higher buildings require a longer period of fire resistance than two or three storey structures.

(ii) The floor area of the building and the distance of any part to a protected means of escape such as a stairwell.

(iii) The capacity and functional use of a building — certain uses being a higher fire risk than others (E5)*.

In addition, all structural elements below ground must be constructed to provide a longer period of fire resistance and, for this purpose, the ground floor construction over a basement is required to be treated as an element below ground (E5).

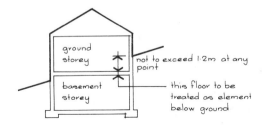

Minimum periods of fire resistance for specific elements of superstructure are as follows (E5):

External walls: ½ hour fire resistance
Separating walls between buildings: 1 hour fire resistance
Compartmenting walls and floors: 1 hour fire resistance (e.g. between flats)

Single storey structures consisting of a structural frame, internal loadbearing walls (except compartmenting and separating walls etc.) and external walls are exempt from these provisions (E5(2)(c)*)

16.06 Durability and weather resistance
The superstructure of a building must be designed and constructed to survive without undue or extensive maintenance for at least the notional life of the

building itself. This period varies with different occupations, some involving industrial and commercial processes which soon become obsolete and require new buildings to house updated plant. In most cases, however, the superstructure can be modified for re-use; it is only the internal non-structural elements and services which are expendable and in the main, are easy to replace.

16.07

It is a primary requirement of all building structures that they are resistant to the weather. Walls must not allow the passage of water falling on their outer surfaces in the form of rain. Moisture rising out of the ground must be stopped by the insertion of an impervious damp proof membrane. Roofs must be constructed not only to prevent the entry of rain or snow but also collect and discharge any water falling on their surfaces clear of the superstructure below and without annoyance to persons using the grounds around the perimeter of the building.

16.08

The Building Regulations lay down precise requirements for the protection of buildings against damp:

(i) All walls must be constructed to avoid moisture from the ground adversely affecting either the materials in the wall itself or the inside of the building (C6/8)*.

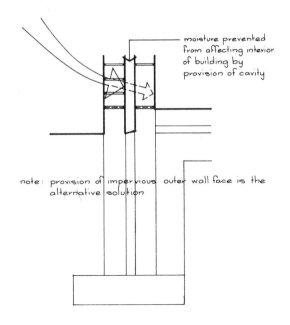

moisture prevented from affecting interior of building by provision of cavity

note: provision of impervious outer wall face is the alternative solution

(iii) Damp proof courses in external walls must be at least 150 mm above adjacent ground level, the cavity in cavity walls to extend at least 150 mm below the lowest d.p.c. and d.p.c.'s in walls must be sealed to any damp proof membranes provided in solid ground floor construction (C7)*.

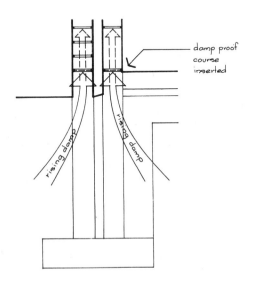

damp proof course inserted

rising damp

rising damp

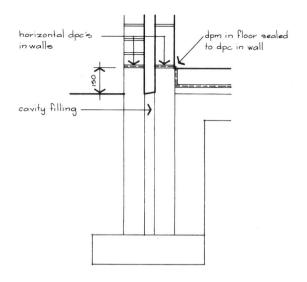

horizontal dpc's in walls

dpm in floor sealed to dpc in wall

150

cavity filling

(ii) External walls must be constructed to avoid moisture from rain or snow adversely affecting the inside of the building (C6/8)*.

(vi) Roofs must be weatherproof (C10)*.

(v) Openings in cavity walls must be so constructed that damp penetration is prohibited at head, reveals and cills (C9)*.

water penetration prevented by insertion of dpm of lead or similarly impervious material to form tray

Section through head of opening in cavity wall

water penetration prevented either by insertion of vertical dpm or by continuing cavity through to back of frame, if provided

Plan of reveal of opening in cavity wall

water penetration prevented by insertion of dpm between outer and inner leaf of cavity wall or by continuing cavity through to underside of cill

Section through cill of opening in cavity wall

16.09

The design of the superstructure of a building in respect of thermal resistance involves controlling heat loss and heat gain and reducing the effect of extreme external temperatures. Control is achieved by increasing the resistance to heat flow by incorporating insulating materials between the interior and the exterior environment. In addition, where roofs are concerned, the addition of light coloured finishes or foil faced felt can be used to reflect solar radiation, control heat gain and reflect irradiation or excessive heat loss which occurs at night under clear cold starlit skies.

solar rays reflected from light coloured or bright metallic surface

solar rays reduced by resistance of insulant

heat generated within building contained by resistance of insulant

16.10

A problem which occurs with buildings of high insulative construction is that of condensation. Warm relatively moist air at high pressure within the building will pass through most building materials such as concrete, brick, blocks or tiles. At some point within the structure this warm moist vapour will meet cold from the outside. When this takes place a condition known as dew point will occur and the excess moisture in the warm vapour will be deposited within the structure. Whereas in cavity wall masonry structures this may not be a serious problem, it may become so where this occurs in solid walls or in flat or low pitched timber roof construction. Consequently, a vapour barrier must be incorporated in the structure to prevent this occurring and this barrier is always placed on the warm or inside surface of the insulative layer.

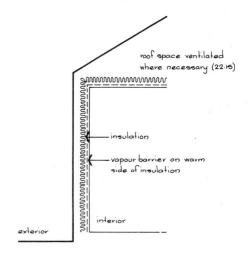

roof space ventilated where necessary (22.15)

insulation

vapour barrier on warm side of insulation

interior

exterior

Care must be taken to ensure that the barrier is continuous without laps or butt joints, any joins which occur must be properly sealed by:

(i) Welting, in the case of thin flexible sheet materials such as 500 gauge polythene.

(ii) Sealing in bitumen, in the case of bitumen felts.

(iii) Sealing by means of an adhesive vapour proof strip, in the case of rigid barriers such as foil backed plasterboard.

16.11

The Building Regulations* lay down specific requirements for the thermal insulation of such buildings as are included in their mandatory provisions. These may be summarised as follows:

(i) Walls separating interior from open air to have U value of not more than 1.0 watts/m² deg C.

(ii) Roofs including ceilings separating interior from open air to have U value of not more than 0.6 watts/m2/degree C.

(iii) Window openings*:

(a) single glazing 5.7 watts/m² /degree C
(b) double glazing 2.8 watts/m² /degree C.　　(F3)

The calculation of average U values for external walling is outside the scope of this syllabus. The Building Regulations (Schedule 11*) do however include a wide range of 'deemed to satisfy' constructions which cover most of the standard eventualities of superstructure design.

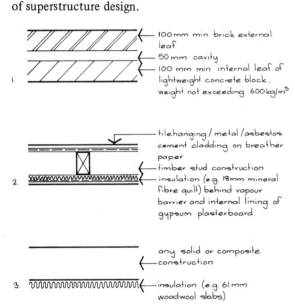

1.
— 100 mm min brick external leaf
— 50 mm cavity
— 100 mm min internal leaf of lightweight concrete block, weight not exceeding 600 kg/m³

2.
— tile hanging / metal / asbestos cement cladding on breather paper
— timber stud construction
— insulation (e.g. 18mm mineral fibre quilt) behind vapour barrier and internal lining of gypsum plasterboard.

3.
— any solid or composite construction
— insulation (e.g. 61mm woodwool slabs)

Examples of wall construction to satisfy insulation requirements of Regulation F4 Schedule 11

16.12

Sound resistance is primarily concerned with the prevention of transmission between dwellings. The principal method for reducing noise transmission is by good planning whereby noisy areas are placed adjacent and quiet areas are separated from these. Sound is, however, generally intermittent in nature and is produced by one of the two ways:

(i) By impact, such as footsteps which cause the structure to vibrate in sympathy on the same frequency.

(ii) By airborne noise, such as voices or radio.

Impact noise can be reduced by the use of a resilient finish to the floor or the incorporation of a soft insulative material to allow the upper surface to float on the structural floor beneath.

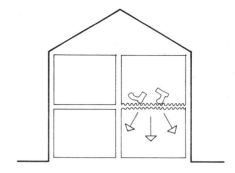

Effect of impact vibrations through floor of building

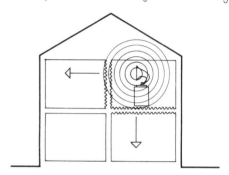

Effect of airborne sound through party wall and floor of building

Airborne noise can only be dampened by mass of structure or by the inclusion of breaks in the structure.

16.13

The sound insulation of walls between separate dwellings is a statutory requirement (C1(1))* and 'deemed to satisfy' requirements are fully described (G2 — Schedule 12)*.

The sound insulation of floors between separate dwellings is also a statutory requirement (G3/4/5)* and 'deemed to satisfy' requirements are also fully described (G4/5 — Schedule 12)*, see illustrations on opposite page.

16.14

In addition to the requirements described above there are a number of other matters which must be given consideration:

(i) The problem of mass or dead load which could be of considerable importance on a site with poor subsoil.

(ii) Speed of construction which could be affected by

(a) Availability of selected materials.
(b) Availability of suitable labour.

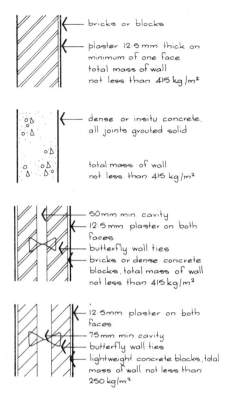

bricks or blocks

plaster 12.5 mm thick on minimum of one face total mass of wall not less than 415 kg/m²

dense or insitu concrete, all joints grouted solid

total mass of wall not less than 415 kg/m²

50 mm min. cavity
12.5 mm plaster on both faces
butterfly wall ties
bricks or dense concrete blocks, total mass of wall not less than 415 kg/m²

12.5 mm plaster on both faces
75 mm min. cavity
butterfly wall ties
lightweight concrete blocks, total mass of wall not less than 250 kg/m²

Examples of separating wall construction between dwellings

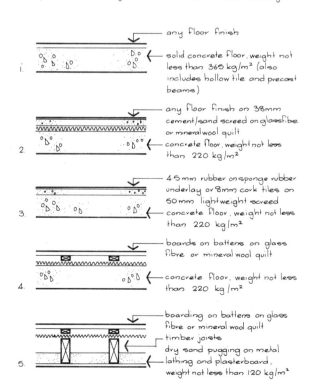

1. any floor finish
solid concrete floor, weight not less than 365 kg/m² (also includes hollow tile and precast beams)

2. any floor finish on 38 mm cement/sand screed on glassfibre or mineral wool quilt
concrete floor, weight not less than 220 kg/m²

3. 4.5 mm rubber on sponge rubber underlay or 8 mm cork tiles on 50 mm lightweight screed
concrete floor, weight not less than 220 kg/m²

4. boards on battens on glass fibre or mineral wool quilt
concrete floor, weight not less than 220 kg/m²

5. boarding on battens on glass fibre or mineral wool quilt
timber joists
dry sand pugging on metal lathing and plasterboard, weight not less than 120 kg/m²

Examples of separating floor construction between dwellings

(c) Site conditions.
(d) Standardisation of components.
(e) Degree of off-site prefabrication.

(iii) The appearance, material selected, its colour and texture and the requirements of the local planning authority.

(iv) The economics of the project, the relationship of cost limits to proposals and the likely return on the capital employed.

17.00 Scaffolding and temporary support

As soon as the superstructure reaches a height of about 1.5 m above the general ground level it is necessary to provide raised platforms so that both the workmen and the materials being used in the construction are brought to a convenient level to the work in hand. These temporary platforms are called scaffolds.

17.01

Scaffolding is constructed from lengths of tubular steel or alloy secured together with steel couplers which are tightened onto the tube by means of a bolt, bolted clips or patented slot fittings. When the end of a tube is required to be built into a brick joint, a special tube is used called a putlog, one end of which has been flattened to fit into the joint.

Vertical tubes are called standards and at the bottom a baseplate is provided to prevent the end of the tube sinking into the ground under load. Horizontal tubes called ledgers are provided parallel to the face of the building to secure the standards together, to support the free ends of the putlogs and to provide guard rails to prevent workmen falling off the scaffold.

17.02

The platforms are formed from specially selected and prepared softwood banded boards, placed side by side and supported on the putlogs. One board is fixed vertically to the inside of the standards and is called a toe board. This prevents workmen from accidentally putting a foot over the edge and also helps to prevent material falling from the platforms. The inner board must be turned back each night or when heavy rain occurs to prevent mortar and mud from the scaffold washing down the face of the wall.

17.03

Two types of scaffold are in general use:

(i) The bricklayer's scaffold which uses the building for partial support by building in the ends of the putlogs to obtain rigidity.

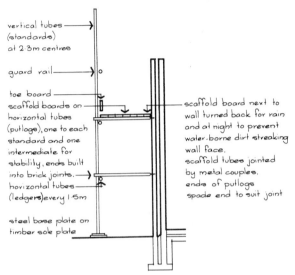

vertical tubes (standards) at 2.3m centres

guard rail

toe board
scaffold boards on horizontal tubes (putlogs), one to each standard and one intermediate for stability, ends built into brick joints.
horizontal tubes (ledgers) every 1.5m

steel base plate on timber sole plate

scaffold board next to wall turned back for rain and at night to prevent water-borne dirt streaking wall face.
scaffold tubes jointed by metal couples.
ends of putlogs spade end to suit joint

Section through typical bricklayers' scaffold

(ii) The mason's scaffold which is independent of the building as regards dead load being provided with two lines of standards and ledgers to support the transome tubes which replace the putlog of the bricklayer's scaffold. For safety this scaffold must be tied into the structure.

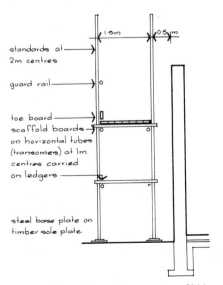

standards at 2m centres

guard rail

toe board
scaffold boards on horizontal tubes (transomes) at 1m centres carried on ledgers

steel base plate on timber sole plate

Section through typical masons' scaffold

When scaffolding is of exceptional size or height diagonal braces are provided to prevent 'racking' and the tendency of the framework to collapse. Access to the platforms is by hoist (for materials only) or ladders. The latter must be set at a convenient angle for use and securely roped to the ledgers to prevent dislodgment and accidents.

17.04

Temporary support is often required during the construction of a building either to:

(i) make safe adjoining structures during the construction of an infill building, or

(ii) to ensure stability of existing structure during the formation of an opening or while alterations are carried out, or

(iii) to support existing openings while temporary support is applied to adjoining areas of the super-structure.

17.05

Where a gap of about 10–12 m wide between two buildings is to be filled in by the construction of a new building it will often be necessary to provide support to the adjoining structures before demolition of the existing structure by temporary works. In this instance a construction known as a 'flying shore' is often used.

This has the advantage of leaving the ground area free for construction and can be fabricated from timber or tubular steel.

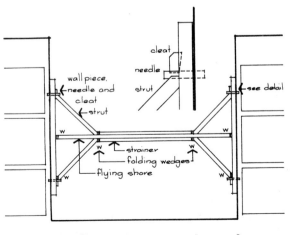

cleat
needle
wall piece.
needle and cleat
strut
strut
see detail
strainer
folding wedges
flying shore

Typical timber flying shore to maximum span of 12m at 2.5m centres

17.06

If the gap is greater, or the adjoining building of some height, the use of a raking shore will be applicable. This form of temporary support not only prevents outward movement but will also take some load from the building being supported.

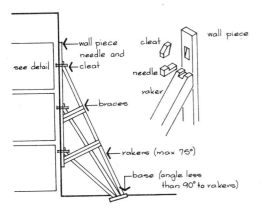

Typical timber raking shore at 2·5m centres

17.07

Where a large opening is to be formal in the lower part of a structure it is necessary to support the floors and walls above the proposed opening to prevent collapse. The floors are first strutted up by the use of vertical timbers and spreaders (with wedges driven in to make all tight and secure) or by the use of expanding steel props and spreaders.

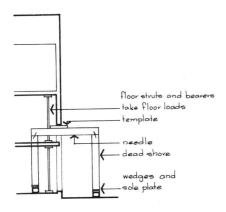

Typical timber dead shore at 1·8m centres

This will support the floor loads and thus reduce the load imposed over the opening. When the structure is secure, holes are cut through the walls and floor immediately over the proposed opening at about 1.8 m centres and large timbers called needles are inserted. The ends of these are supported on similar large timbers called dead shores and all are wedged up

tight against the tops of the openings in the walls. This is carried out by inserting wedges between the ends of the shore and large timbers placed along the ground or on the solid ground floor and called sole plates.

Needles are always inserted under structural piers between windows to provide maximum support.

17.08

Where existing windows occur in areas adjacent to shoring, these form a potential weakness in the wall. Consequently they must be strutted up to prevent the reveals collapsing across the opening.

Typical timber strutting to openings close to areas where shoring is carried out

18.00 Function and construction of external brick walls

In most building contracts the substructure of the building is completed before any move is made to commence work on the superstructure. The reasons for this are that materials used in the substructure usually differ in composition due to the need for greater resistance to damp in the ground and the need to level up the structure all round at some predetermined level so that the superstructure can be erected on a level base. A convenient point for this is that at which the damp proof course is inserted in the structure and it is at this point that the superstructure generally commences.

18.01

The statutory requirements for damp proof courses to prevent rising damp from the ground have been given before in paragraph 16.08 (iii). Other locations where protection is required are in parapet walls and chimney stacks. These are dealt with in detail in their appropriate paragraphs.

The most important features of a damp proof course (dpc) have been fully described (15.06). In addition

the material should have a good resistance to loading without crushing or extrusion from the joint.
Material for the dpc's described (15.06) can be classified into three categories:

(i) *Flexible*. Suitable for most locations and especially for bridging cavities and at head of openings (lead, copper, bitumen felt and polythene to BS 743, pitch/polymer)

(ii) *Semi-rigid*. Suitable for thick walls and where water pressure is present (mastic asphalt)

(iii) *Rigid*. Suitable for very heavy loads but can be fractured by building movement (epoxy resin/sand, engineering bricks and slates)

18.02

In most cases the following materials are in general use for low rise building constructed in traditional materials:

Horizontal dpc's in masonry and brick walls	Bitumen felt pitch polymer Code 4. lead
Reveals of openings in cavity walls	Bitumen felt pitch polymer
Dpc's to heads of openings and where cavity is bridged	Pitch polymer Code 4. lead
Dpc's, either horizontal or vertical, where water pressure is present, (e.g. in ground floor and basement walls and floors)	Mastic asphalt

Care must be taken to ensure continuity, otherwise water will penetrate. Flexible dpc's must be jointed in their length by overlapping at the ends by at least 100 mm and similarly at angles (16.08).

Semi rigid dpc's must be laid in at least two coat thicknesses with joins finished staggered 150 mm for horizontal and 75 mm for vertical work. All internal angles are provided with an angle fillet at least 50 mm wide.

Rigid dpc's are either laid as a continuous layer about 6 mm thick (epoxy resin/sand) or in the case of engineering bricks or slate, two course laid breaking joint in cement mortar 1:3.

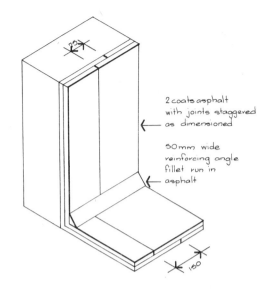

2 coats asphalt with joints staggered as dimensioned

50 mm wide reinforcing angle fillet run in asphalt

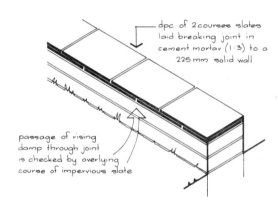

dpc of 2 courses slates laid breaking joint in cement mortar (1:3) to a 225 mm solid wall

passage of rising damp through joint is checked by overlying course of impervious slate

Typical slate rigid dpc to a brick wall

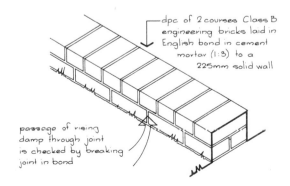

dpc of 2 courses Class B engineering bricks laid in English bond in cement mortar (1:3) to a 225mm solid wall

passage of rising damp through joint is checked by breaking joint in bond

Typical engineering brick dpc to a brick wall

18.03

Damp proof courses can become ineffectual for a number of reasons:

(i) They can fracture or tear and this allows damp to pass.

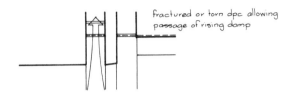

fractured or torn dpc allowing passage of rising damp

(ii) They can be bridged by one of several means:

(a) by soil banked up externally over the level of the dpc;

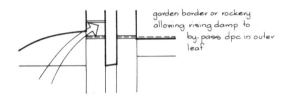

garden border or rockery allowing rising damp to by-pass dpc in outer leaf

(b) by mortar droppings falling down the cavity; as the work proceeds and building up on damp course projecting into the cavity;

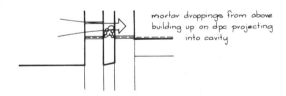

mortar droppings from above building up on dpc projecting into cavity

(c) by rendering applied to the exterior of the super-structure which passes over the dpc.

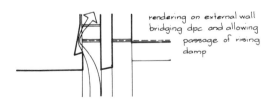

rendering on external wall bridging dpc and allowing passage of rising damp

All foundation walls to receive flexible dpc's are flushed up with a thin layer of cement and sand mortar (1:3) to provide a level bed for the material. The next course of bricks or blocks is then bedded in a similar mortar onto the dpc.

18.04

External walls are required to be constructed to conform to a number of criteria discussed in detail in Module E, Section 16.00. 'Deemed to satisfy' requirements of the Building Regulations form the basis of the following constructional details:

(i) *Structural stability*. Walls built of bricks or blocks have a reasonable resistance to vertical loading but little to lateral thrust. Their strength here lies in the relationship of thickness to height. In most domestic structures up to three stories in height with a floor to ceiling height to each storey of about 2.4 m, the external wall should have an overall material thickness of 225 mm (as in 275 mm cavity wall).

While all brick or block walls have continuous horizontal (bedding) joints, to increase resistance to failure from vertical loading, the vertical joints (perpends) are staggered to increase strength. In addition the arrangement of the vertical joints (bond) can be selected to provide an attractive appearance to the wall itself. The amount of the stagger (lap) varies from a quarter to half a brick stretcher depending on the type of bond selected. Bonds used in various thicknesses of walls are as follows:

Stretcher bond. Suitable for half brick thick walls and for the separate leaves of 275 mm cavity walls.

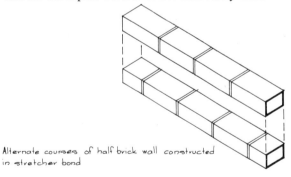

Alternate courses of half brick wall constructed in stretcher bond

English bond. Suitable only for walls 225 mm thick and over. The wall constructed in this bond has exceptional strength but its visual appearance is poor.

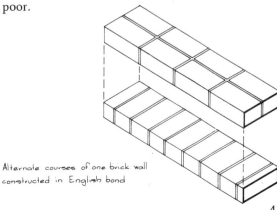

Alternate courses of one brick wall constructed in English bond

Flemish bond. Suitable for walls 225 mm thick and over. A traditional decorative bond especially when the header is of a different colour to the stretcher face.

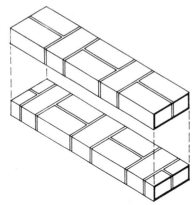

Alternate courses of one brick wall constructed in Flemish bond

Garden wall bond. (*Flemish*) Suitable for walls of half brick thickness (with some cutting) and 225 mm thick. Often used instead of stretcher bond for external skins of cavity walls in good class work.

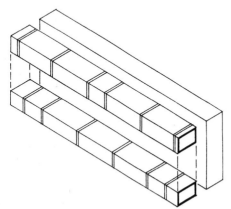

Alternate courses of half brick external skin of cavity wall constructed in Flemish garden wall bond (3 stretchers to each header)

18.05

Brickwork is built to a 'gauge', i.e. the number of courses to be built in a fixed height, such as four courses to 300 mm.

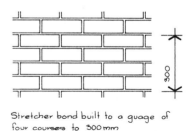

Stretcher bond built to a guage of four courses to 300 mm

At corners the brickwork is raised to a greater height than the centre of the wall to enable the bricklayer to set up his line and ensure all courses are level and plumb on the face. The stepped arrangement is used called 'raking back'.

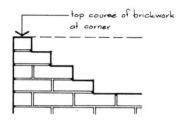

Raking back at quoin or corner of wall built in stretcher bond

When a wall is to be bonded to another to be constructed later at right angles to the first, the alternate courses are set forward and back (toothing) to ensure proper bonding in due course. Alternatively block bonding — three courses in and three courses out — is employed.

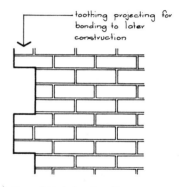

Typical block bonding for half brick wall

When a wall is to receive another along its length at right angles. 'indents' are left in the face to allow the wall to be properly bonded to the first. When block partitions are to be constructed 'block bonding' is usually followed.

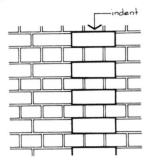

Elevation of one brick wall in English bond showing indents for one brick wall to be constructed later at right angles to the first

18.06

(ii) *Weather resistance*. Weather resistance of external walls will vary with rainfall, exposure and material used. While in some areas external walls of 225 mm thick solid brick provide satisfactory resistance to water penetration, they do not satisfy modern requirements for thermal resistance (16.10). Consequently the use of walls constructed with a cavity between 50 and 75 mm in width have been used successfully for fifty years, the cavity providing a satisfactory barrier to water penetrating through the outer skin of the wall itself.

18.07

Cavity walls for domestic buildings can be constructed in a number of ways, all of which comply, so far as the Building Regulations are concerned, with the requirements for structural stability (19.01):

(i) External leaf of brick with inner leaf of light weight blocks providing a wall of total thickness of 275 mm.

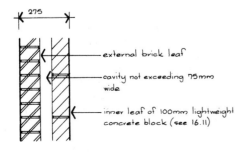

- external brick leaf
- cavity not exceeding 75mm wide
- inner leaf of 100mm lightweight concrete block (see 16.11)

(ii) External and internal leafs of light weight block, the external face protected from the weather by either

(a) tile hanging; or
(b) weatherboarding; or
(c) rendering in cement/lime/sand (1:1:6).

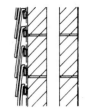

265 x 165 mm plain tiles each nailed to 38 x 19mm impregnated softwood sawn battens at 100mm centres nailed through building paper to lightweight block walls

(a) tile hanging

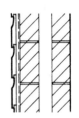

150 x 25 mm impregnated softwood weatherboarding nailed to 38 x 19mm impregnated softwood sawn battens at 1400mm centres nailed through building paper to lightweight block walls

(b) weatherboarding

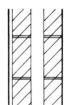

25 mm thick 1:1:6 cement/ lime/sand rendering applied in two coats with open texture finish to lightweight block walls

(c) rendering

18.08

(iii) *Thermal resistance*. The use of a cavity in providing weather resistance to a wall helps to increase its thermal resistance. The Building Regulations lay down precise requirements for the thermal resistance of external walls (16.10) and 'deemed to satisfy' requirements for cavity walls are as follows:

External leaf of brick/50 mm cavity (min)/inner leaf of concrete block with density not exceeding 60 kg/m3.

This construction closely follows the requirements for both weather resistance and for structural stability. The addition of tile hanging or weatherboarding to the external face will materially assist in increasing the thermal resistance of the wall.

18.09

(iv) *External appearance*. So far as is practical the use of different materials to enhance the external appearance of the building should follow local usage and traditional construction. Decorative brick bonds enliven brickwork too often rendered uninteresting by the use of stretcher bond. Tilehung panels and first floor finish is common in many areas of south-east England. Weatherboarding is common in Kent, Surrey and Essex. Rendering is found throughout England from Cornwall, through Dorset and Wiltshire to East Anglia. Modern constructional techniques ensure that these finishes are both practical and attractive (18.07).

18.10

(v) *Wall ties*. While cavity walls are satisfactory for the external walls of buildings in respect of weather and thermal resistance, the employment of two relatively thin skins of brick or block instead of a solid bonded structure of comparable gross thickness requires some lateral tie between the two. This is to ensure that loads imposed on the inner leaf from roof and floors will be evenly distributed throughout both leaves.

The Building Regulations (D15/16 – Schedule 7)* require that the two leaves be tied together by the use of approved ties. The approved types in general use are:

(a) Galvanised wire butterfly pattern.

(b) Plastic pattern of patent design.

(c) Galvanised wrot iron vertical twist pattern.

The latter is much stronger than the other two and, when spaced at a closer spacing horizontally (750 mm) than the Regulations provide, will allow the width of the cavity to be increased to 100 mm.

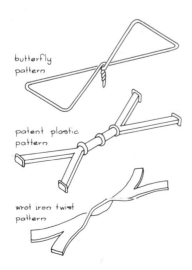

butterfly pattern

patent plastic pattern

wrot iron twist pattern

The normal maximum spacing of wall ties in cavities from 50/75 mm wide is as follows:

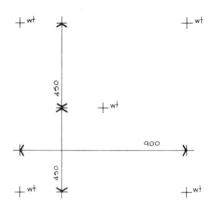

Elevation showing spacing of wall ties to cavity wall

In addition the reveals of openings must be provided with additional wall ties every 300 mm in height to ensure stability at these points.

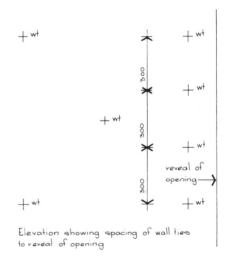

Elevation showing spacing of wall ties to reveal of opening

18.11

(vi) *Mortar*. In addition to bonding, bricks and blocks are bedded in mortar to increase the stability of the wall. The design of a mortar mix should ensure:

(a) Good bond between bricks or blocks and mortar.

(b) Early strength especially in winter to resist frost.

(c) Strength of mortar should be less than brick or block — otherwise any movement due to shrinkage in the brick or block, thermal expansion or settlement, will result in the block or brick cracking. Ideally all cracks should be contained within the mortar joint.

The choice of mortar should restrict the cement content to a minimum, although richer mixes are usually required in winter to obtain earlier strength to resist the attack of frost.

18.12 Mortars in common use are:

(i) *Cement mortar.* 1:3 (cement/sand) for foundations, manholes and chimneys above the roof line.

(ii) *Air entrained (plasticised) mortar.* Increases the working qualities of lean cement/sand mixes — thus a 1:6 cement and sand mix with the addition of a plasticiser is a good alternative to mix (iv)

(iii) *Masonry cement mortar* A mixture of Portland cement with a fine mineral filler and an air entraining additive — usually 1:4 cement/sand comparable to 1:3 cement/sand mix.

(iv) *Cement-lime mortar* Known as compo motar. Produces a mortar with good working properties, water retention and bonding. Develops early strength. Lime should be non-hydraulic to BS 890. Generally used in 1:1:6 cement/lime sand mix for all cavity and superstructure brick walling and internal blockwork above dpc level.

Schedule 11 Parts II and III of the Scottish Regulations gives specifications for mortar mixes for particular purposes and degrees of exposure.

18.13

Bricks are laid in mortar spread along the top of a wall. The pressure of laying the brick causes some of the mortar to exude from the joint and this excess has to be removed while it is still fresh and wet. Mortar joints are finished in two ways:

(i) By jointing the freshly exuded mortar with the point or side of the trowel or the use of a special tool. A number of different types of joint can be produced as follows:

(a) Flush joint cut off with the side of the trowel and the surface of the mortar lightly raised by brushing with a soft brush — the best joint for facing work as the mortar is not compressed but is similar in texture to the bedding mortar.

(b) Ironed joint produced from the end of a rounded rod — the surface of the mortar is pressed in and the texture is altered.

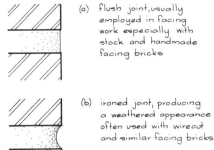

(a) Flush joint, usually employed in facing work especially with stock and handmade facing bricks

(b) ironed joint, producing a weathered appearance often used with wirecut and similar facing bricks

(c) struck or weathered joint, poor appearance and weather resistance

Examples of common jointing techniques

(c) Struck or weathered joint formed by the point of the trowel — weather resistance is poor.

(ii) By pointing which involves raking out the partly set mortar from the joint and replacing this on completion of the face brickwork with fresh mortar. Coloured mortars are usually applied in this way.

mortar raked out and replaced by fresh mortar, often coloured

Jointing is quicker and cheaper than pointing but unless great care is taken over the preparation of all the mortar used, uneven colour can ensue. Pointing can be more even and attractive but there is a greater risk of frost getting behind the pointing and forcing this out of the joint.

19.00 Openings in external walls

Openings in external walls are required for a number of reasons. These are

(i) for access into and out of the building;

(ii) to provide natural daylighting to the interior;

(iii) to provide natural ventilation for the inhabitants;

(iv) to enable users of the building to enjoy a view of the surrounding countryside.

Generally speaking, a solid wall of any construction is cheaper than the formation and enclosure of an opening and therefore large windows are rarely economic in low cost buildings.

In addition, the Building Regulations require that the number, size and position of opening shall not impair the stability of any wall (D15/16—Schedule 7, Rule 6)*.

19.01

It is a structural requirement that the loads applied to the walling above all openings must be adequately contained and transferred to the walling on either side (reveal) of the opening by means of a lintol.

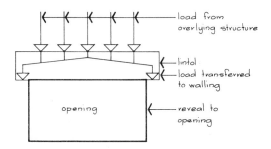

Brickwork by virtue of its construction is partially self supporting and in most cases it is only the dead load of the material plus any superimposed loading from the floors within the area of an equilateral triangle whose base is formed by the underside (soffite) of the opening which needs to be taken into account in calculating the size of the lintol — the rest of the walling is self supporting.

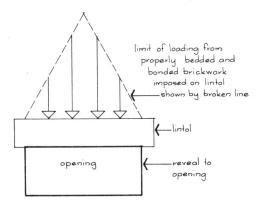

Care must be taken to ensure that the materials forming the perimeter of the openings are solidly and soundly constructed. The supporting work (lintol) should have sufficient bearing to transmit the loads onto the wall and the reveals in cavity work provided with extra wall ties (18.10). Minimum bearing for lintols should be 150 mm.

19.02

The sequence of work to form a window or door opening is to bring the wall up to course level at the underside of the cill and then continue the reveals up to the level of the underside of the lintol, first fixing the window in position and strutting this up until the reveals are completed. The supporting work over is then constructed including any damp proof course and temporary support to the external leaf of the cavity wall. Lastly the cill is constructed to the bottom of the window or, if this is integral with the window frame itself, the brick courses left down are put in together with any damp proof course required under the cill.

19.03

(i) *Sills*. There are a number of different methods which may be adopted to finish the bottom of an opening for either a door (threshold) or a window. All have one object in common, to collect storm-water running down the impervious face of the glass, metal or timber, and throwing this clear of the wall below without allowing any to penetrate to the building.

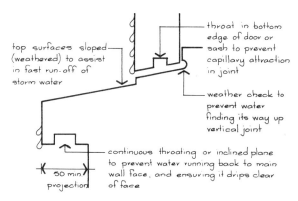

Some types of sill are often used in conjunction with particular methods for providing support to the head of the openings:

(i) Brick-on-edge weathered sill (often used with brick flat soldier arches and generally used for sills to doorways).

(ii) Tile creased sill (same uses as (i)).

(iii) Precast concrete or natural stone (boot lintol or rubbed flat arch).

(iv) Projecting wood sill integral with timber window frame (pressed steel lintol).

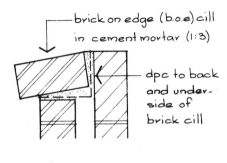

brick on edge (b.o.e) cill in cement mortar (1:3)

dpc to back and underside of brick cill

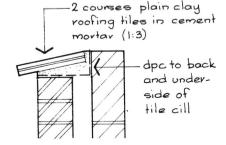

2 courses plain clay roofing tiles in cement mortar (1:3)

dpc to back and underside of tile cill

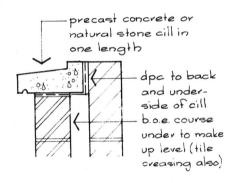

precast concrete or natural stone cill in one length

dpc to back and underside of cill

b.o.e. course under to make up level (tile creasing also)

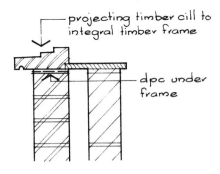

projecting timber cill to integral timber frame

dpc under frame

19.04

(ii) *Reveals*. Unless there are any special reasons to the contrary, reveals to openings should be closed by returning the blockwork forming the inner leaf of the wall across the cavity and butting this against a

dpc (18.02). If a flexible material is used this should be at least 150 mm wide and either tacked to the back of the timber frame and set to pass into the cavity or set tight into the back rebate of the steel window frame.

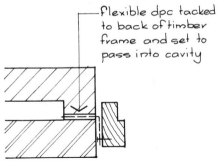

flexible dpc tacked to back of timber frame and set to pass into cavity

Plan of reveal to door with timber frame

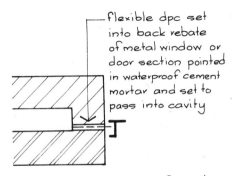

flexible dpc set into back rebate of metal window or door section pointed in waterproof cement mortar and set to pass into cavity

Plan of reveal to window formed from standard metal sections

Care must be taken to ensure that the dpc is turned over and built into the underside of the lintol and hangs down into the cavity below the cill. All dpc's to reveals should be in continuous lengths and not joined. Rigid dpc's of slate in cement mortar may be used instead of the method outlined above, in addition to plastic cavity fillers.

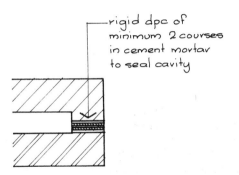

rigid dpc of minimum 2 courses in cement mortar to seal cavity

Plan of reveal with solid cavity closer

47

19.05

(iii) *Lintols*. There are a number of adequate methods of supporting the cavity wall over the opening. In cavity walls care must be taken to ensure that water flowing down the inner face of the outer leaf is collected *over* the supporting work and diverted to the outside. Lead (standard Code 4 lead) is generally used for this purpose. This protection is referred to as a cavity 'tray', the ends of which must project at least 50 mm beyond the reveal support and be turned up to prevent water running off the end into the cavity. Every third perpend in the brickwork over the tray is left open to allow water to escape.

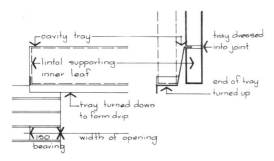

Typical weatherproofing to head of opening in brick cavity wall

19.06

The following examples of lintols are in general use:

(i) Rectangular reinforced concrete lintol the full thickness of the wall. (This no longer complies with the thermal requirements of the Building Regulations for external walls to domestic structures).

(ii) Continuous reinforced concrete lintol with nib to carry external leaf of brickwork (boot lintol).

(iii) Reinforced concrete lintol supporting inner leaf with galvanised pressed steel lintol carrying external leaf of wall.

(iv) Galvanised pressed steel lintol carrying both inner and outer leaves of cavity wall.

(v) Reinforced concrete lintol carrying internal leaf with flat brick arch supporting external leaf with mild steel angle support.

(vi) As (v), but with external leaf of brickwork reinforced with galvanised mild steel mesh incorporated in brick courses.

(vii) Reinforced concrete lintol carrying internal leaf with rubbed or cut brick arch supporting external leaf of brickwork.

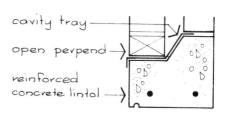

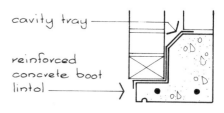

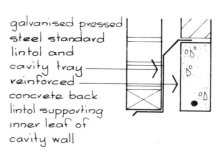

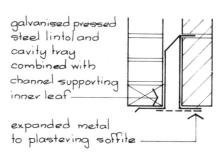

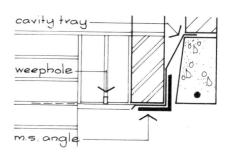

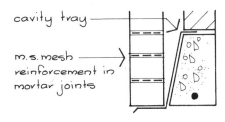

cavity tray

m.s. mesh reinforcement in mortar joints

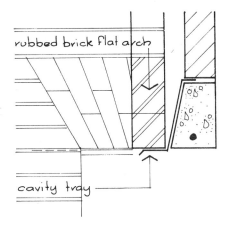

rubbed brick flat arch

cavity tray

Concrete for reinforced work of this nature is generally specified as a nominal mix proportioned by volume. For lintols and small suspended slabs two mixes are in general use:

1:2:4 (one part Portland cement; two parts fine aggregate (sand): four parts coarse aggregate to pass a 19 mm mesh).
1:1½:3 (one part of Portland cement: one and one half parts fine aggregate: three parts coarse aggregate to pass a 19 mm mesh).

The second mix is stronger and might well be used in cold weather when a faster set is required. The aggregate size is reduced to ensure that it can be well worked around the steel reinforcement, especially when the cover to the steel is only 25 mm. The volume of material required for each mix/50 kg cement is as follows:

	Fine aggregate (m^3)	Coarse aggregate (m^3)
1:2:4	0.07	0.14
1:1½:3	0.05	0.10

(See also Substructure – 12.08(iv))

19.07

Reinforced concrete lintols can be constructed in two ways:

(i) *In situ* by forming a wooden box on top of the wall, inserting the steel reinforcement and filling the box up with concrete; and

(ii) by casting the lintol on the ground in a box shutter and hoisting into position after the concrete has hardened and the box removed. Care must be taken to mark the top of the lintol so that it is not inserted upside down.

Marking the top of precast lintols is important, as the reinforcing steel is placed in the bottom of the lintol to provide maximum resistance to bending moments. Reversing this would cause cracks and failure in the underside of the concrete lintol.

Reinforcement is generally provided by mild steel rods with hooked ends to increase adhesion to the concrete. The bars are usually provided one to each leaf or 112 mm width of wall and of sufficient length to bear onto the reveals by at least 100 mm. A minimum of 25 mm concrete cover is provided under the bars to comply with the requirements of fire resistance.

19.08

Internally, the bottom of the window opening is finished to provide a level, impervious and sometimes decorative surface. This is known as a window board although materials other than timber are often used. The board is usually fixed prior to plastering and the plaster made up to it on all sides. Types of window board are as follows:-

(i) Wrot softwood (i.e. wood which has been planed and thicknessed (11.06)) 25 mm thick, cross tongued where the width exceeds 225 mm and with the free edge slightly rounded. The timber should be primed

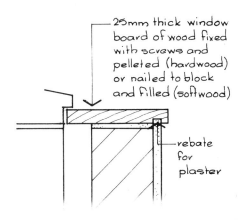

25mm thick window board of wood fixed with screws and pelleted (hardwood) or nailed to block and filled (softwood)

rebate for plaster

on all faces before fixing with a good quality wood primer. Hardwood is sometimes used and finished with a varnish or polyurethane lacquer to show the natural grain. Hardwood window boards must be sealed on all faces before plastering is carried out to avoid staining.

(ii) Quarry tiles either 225 x 225 x 25 mm thick or 150 x 150 x 15 mm thick. These are bedded in cement mortar 1:3 and pointed in white cement. The free edge usually employs a round edge tile known as a 'bullnose'.

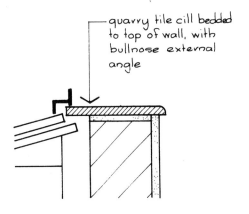

quarry tile cill bedded to top of wall, with bullnose external angle

(iii) Glazed ceramic tiles about 6 mm thick and of various sizes to match and marry up with wall tiling. Bedded as for quarry tiles, ceramic tiles are pointed with a special grout.

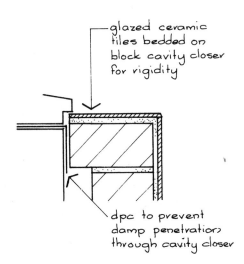

glazed ceramic tiles bedded on block cavity closer for rigidity

dpc to prevent damp penetration through cavity closer

20.00 Internal walls and partitions

Internal walls and partitions can be either load-bearing or mere dividers of space. A wide variety of materials is available to suit various circumstances and particular requirements. All must conform to one or all of the following:

(i) Loadbearing partitions and separating walls must be provided with a foundation to adequate transmit both dead and superimposed loads to a satisfactory bearing strata. It is not necessary to take these foundations down to the same depth as those provided for external walls as the problems of climatic influence (frost heave — shrinkage and expansion due to variable moisture content) do not apply under buildings (13.13). It is necessary, however, to ensure that the underside of the foundation is in solid strata and at abutments to external walls the concrete foundation is supported on a column of concrete resting on the foundation below. Non loadbearing partitions can be built off the oversite concrete slab, this being thickened out to 150 mm.

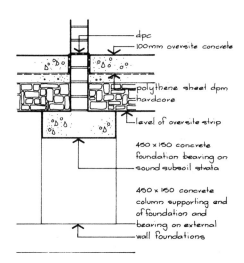

dpc
100mm oversite concrete
polythene sheet dpm
hardcore
level of oversite strip
450 x 150 concrete foundation bearing on sound subsoil strata
450 x 150 concrete column supporting end of foundation and bearing on external wall foundations

Typical foundation for a half brick loadbearing partition

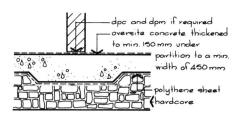

dpc and dpm if required
oversite concrete thickened to min. 150mm under partition to a min. width of 450 mm
polythene sheet
hardcore

Typical foundation for a lightweight block non-loadbearing partition (see also 13.13)

(ii) All partitions (whether loadbearing or not) constructed off the solid ground floor or oversite concrete must be provided with a dpc properly joined to that laid over the concrete slab and to the external walls (15.09).

The requirements of the Building Regulations in respect of foundations and damp courses given before apply equally to internal walls and partitions.

20.01

The selection of material and the thickness of the constructed partition will depend on a number of factors:

(i) Imposed loading from floors and roof.

(ii) Height (relative to structural stability).

(iii) Fire resistance.

(iv) Sound insulation.

These factors have been dealt with before with respect to the requirements of the Building Regulations. Materials in common use are as follows:

(i) Brickwork, usually half brick (112 mm) in thickness providing satisfactory stability up to two floors in height for domestic construction. Brick partitions have a notional fire resistance of two hours (½b thick) but require a foundation to support their weight (13.12).

(ii) Concrete blockwork made from a wide variety of aggregates to BS 2028 giving densities from 600/1400 kg/m³. The usual size of block is 440 x 215 mm. and common thicknesses in use are 215, 150, 100 and 75 mm. For domestic buildings the two last thicknesses are in general use. Light-weight blocks can be used on timber upper floors but it is usual to provide double joists underneath and lay the blocks on a sawn timber sole plate, the width of the block, well nailed down through the boarding into the joists below.

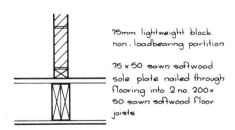

Typical detail of support for non-loadbearing partition on upper timber floor

(iii) Timber stud partitions are commonly used for the framework of partitions on upper floors also constructed of timber. Usually 100 mm in thickness, they are constructed of 75 mm wide sawn timbers with head and sill members securely fixed to floor and ceiling and filled in with vertical timber studs at 400 mm centres and intermediate noggings every 1200 mm in height, to suit width and length of plaster lath finishing. The framework is usually covered with 9.5 mm plasterboard lath which is then finished with a skim coat of neat board plaster finish. Where additional sound insulation is required the studding can be staggered, the head and sill members insulated from the structure by resiliant mountings and the intervening space filled with a layer of sound absorbing quilt.

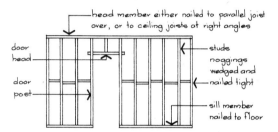

Typical layout for stud partition incorporating opening for door and lining

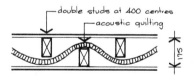

Typical plan of double stud acoustic partition

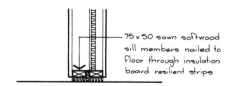

Typical section through partition at floor level (ceiling detail similar)

(iv) A number of proprietory plasterboard partitions are manufactured. The best known employs two 9.5 mm thicknesses of plasterboard separated by a paper honeycomb layer giving a total thickness of 65 mm. These panels are set over a timber cill piece fixed to the floor and secured at the head by a timber batten nailed to the ceiling and timber cornice pieces.

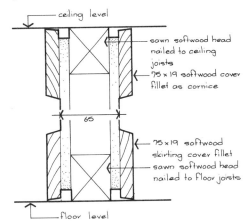

Typical head and sill fixing details of proprietary plasterboard partition

20.02

Bonding and mortars for structural partitions are generally as described before for external walls. These may be summarised as follows:

Work below dpc	1:3 cement/sand mortar
Brickwork and high density blockwork above dpc	1:1:6 cement/lime/ sand mortar
Light weight blockwork	1:2:9 cement/lime/sand mortar

Joints in brick partitions should be raked out to provide a key for plaster or a special grooved common brick used. Generally blockwork will provide a satisfactory surface for plastering without further treatment of joints.

20.03

Openings in internal walls and partitions require support over, for reasons explained for external walls. No problems of damp are, however, to be met and the lintol is generally provided as a single member through the whole thickness of the wall. Certain problems occur and these are summarised as follows:

(i) Concrete, brick or blockwork have different shrinkage coefficients and consequently there is a tendency for cracking to occur both in the mortar joint around concrete lintols and subsequently in the plaster coating. The joint should be covered with expanded metal lath when the finish is plaster.

A similar problem can occur if a mixture of brick and blockwork is permitted in partitions. This can occur under supports for upper timber floors where block courses do not coincide with the underside of timber joists and brickwork is used instead for one or two courses. Horizontal cracking of the plaster surface inevitably occurs.

(ii) Dense concrete provides a poor key for plaster. The surface should be roughened, either by the use of a retarder in the mould (which allows the green concrete to be easily hand roughened), by hacking with a mechanical tool or by the application of a bonding agent which on drying produces a rough surface. These problems also apply to lintols over openings in external walls.

20.04

Methods of supporting openings in internal walls and partitions are as follows:

(i) Precast or *in situ* concrete lintol with minimum bearing of 150 mm and reinforced with 1 No. mild steel bar with hooked ends of suitable diameter for each half brick thickness of wall.

(ii) Flat mild steel arch bar with six courses of brickwork over reinforced with galvanised steel brick reinforcement.

(iii) Commerical galvanised pressed steel lintol built into reveals.

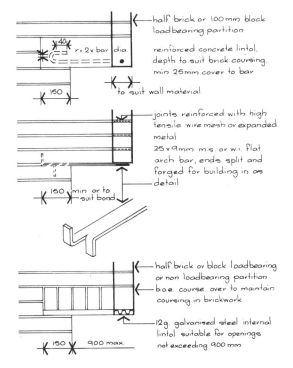

21.00 Timber flooring

Timber floors are in general use in domestic construction, invariably for first floors and for about 50% of ground floor construction. Imported softwood is the material in general use, finished sawn to size from the mill. Softwood for structural purposes in building must comply in all respects with CP 112 *The structural use of timber*, and the measurement of characteristics affecting strength must be measured in accordance with BS 4978:1973 *Timber grades for structural use*.

21.01

The requirements of the Code of Practice and the British Standard can be summarised as follows:-

(i) The following species of softwood are allowed to be used for structural work under the CP and Building Regulations D14(b) Schedule 6* — Douglas Fir, Western Hemlock, pitch pine, redwood, whitewood, larch and Scots pine.

(ii) Timber for structural use shall be stress graded which provides for preferred sizes and defines the qualities of timber to enable it to comply with the structural grades. Two types of grading are recognised, *'visual'* which relies on the expertise of the grader handling the timber and *'machine'* which applies specific stresses to the section and automatically records its reaction. Each grading includes two standards as follows:

Visual stress grading	Machine stress grading
GS (General Structural Grade)	MGS (Machine General Structural)
SS (Special Structural Grade)	MSS (Machine Special Structural)

Stress graded timbers are marked on at least one face, or edge or end.

(iii) Timber for structural work requires a moisture content applicable to its structural location. European softwood is generally dried to a moisture content below 23% before shipment to the UK but softwood from North America is generally unseasoned. Wood is less prone to decay if its moisture content is below 25% and is reasonably immune below 20%. As timber shrinks when drying; the moisture content should be close to its optimum if shrinkage in its final position is not to have an adverse effect on the structure. Fortunately timber tends to shrink mostly across the grain and has little tendency to shrink in its length — this being helpful for structural members. CP 112 requires the following moisture content percentages:

Position in building	Average m/c in dried out structure	Average m/c at time of erection
Rafters, roof boarding and battens	15	22
Upper floor joists	15	22
Ground floor joists	18	22
Site framing/sheathing, etc	16	22

(iv) Tolerances on sawn sizes to nominal sizes must not exceed the following:

Nominal dimension (mm)	Maximum variations (mm)	
	Minus	Plus
25–50	1.5	3.0
51–150	3.0	6.5
150–305	6.5	6.5
Over 305	6.5	12.5

(v) The minimum number of growth rings for each 25 mm of growth, commencing generally from 25 mm from the pith for all grades of timber, must not be less than 4.

(vi) Natural defects in timber include fissures and knots, both of which can form areas of weakness in structural timbers. The permitted size of each defect is defined.

(vii) When logs are sawn (converted) in the sawmill into building timbers, some sections are produced in which one of the angles (arrises) is rounded forming a part of the original outside of the log. This defect is known as wane and while not organically unsound, produces a section which has less strength than its nominal size suggests. The extent of permitted wane is defined.

21.02

Timber, being an organic material, is affected by damp (causing rot) and also certain wood boring insects. Both of these cause loss of strength in structural timber which may lead to collapse. In addition certain parts of England in the Surrey/Berkshire/Hampshire area are severely affected by the borer known as the house longhorn beetle. The Building Regulations require that all softwoods used in roof construction in these areas shall be treated with a water borne copper/chrome/arsenic composition in accordance with BS 4072:1966. This treatment is carried out either by

(a) the full cell vacuum and pressure impregnation process, or

(b) the Lowry empty-cell pressure impregnation process.

As the situation and exposure to hazard of the timber will require varying degrees of salt retention. These are defined interior timbers and must be treated as follows:

Description	Hazard	Example	Average net dry salt retention kg/m3
Interior timbers	Fungal decay and insect attack	Carcassing timbers	4.0

While the regulations only require treatment in localised areas, the relatively small cost compared with the cost of replacing defective timbers suggests that all structural timbers and external joinery should be treated by impregnation before being incorporated in a new building.

21.03

The requirements of the Building Regulations against rising damp in buildings has been discussed previously (15.00) with regard specifically to suspended timber ground floors. Regulations C4/5 define precisely the construction which would prevent rising damp affecting the structural timbers*.

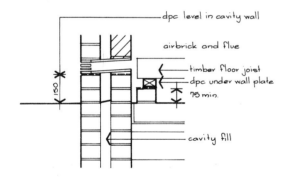

As this shows, a void is required under the timber joists to keep these free from contact with the oversite concrete which may well allow moisture to be drawn out of the ground. In addition the ends of the timbers are kept about 25 mm from the face of the inner leaf as is the wall plate on which the ends of the joists rest. To ensure that the air in the void does not stagnate, air is introduced around the perimeter of the building by building into the outer leaf of the cavity wall immediately under the dpc a 275 x 75 mm perforated brick formed from terracotta ware or precast concrete and forming a flue from slate or asbestos cement through the wall into the void.

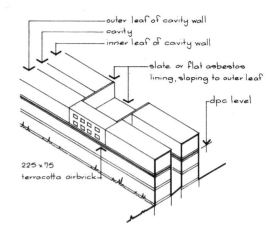

These air bricks should be provided at intervals of not more than 2 m around the perimeter of the building, care being taken to ensure that all voids are cross ventilated. Where solid floors form part of the ground floor construction it may be necessary to provide a duct under the concrete floor to ensure proper cross ventilation.

21.04

Timber joists forming ground floors are supported on low brick walls known as sleeper walls. In practice today these are rarely more than one course of brickwork high and on top is bedded a dpc similar to that provided to the walls of the building. As structural timbers need to be fixed with a perfectly level upper surface to receive the selected flooring, a softwood wall plate is bedded onto the dpc with its surface level to receive the ends of the joists which are nailed down to it. To reduce the size of timber joists required it is usual to provide sleeper walls at intervals of approximately 2 m across the void to reduce the span and provide support.

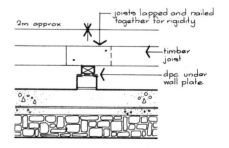

Where solid and suspended timber floors abut, care must be taken to ensure continuity of damp course so that bridging by rising damp cannot occur. Where the ground is sloping and there is consequently a deep void under the joists it may be cheaper to

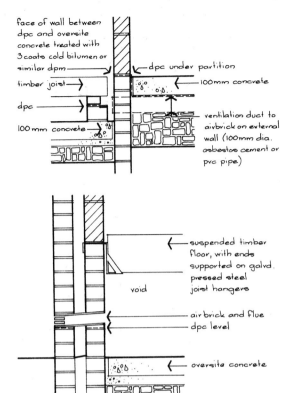

face of wall between dpc and oversite concrete treated with 3 coats cold bitumen or similar dpm

dpc under partition

timber joist

100mm concrete

dpc

ventilation duct to airbrick on external wall (100mm dia. asbestos cement or pvc pipe)

100 mm concrete

suspended timber floor, with ends supported on galvd. pressed steel joist hangers

void

airbrick and flue

dpc level

oversite concrete

note : maximum filling under floors not to exceed 600mm thick

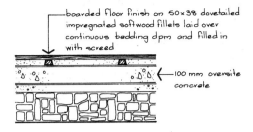

boarded floor finish on 50x38 dovetailed impregnated softwood fillets laid over continuous bedding dpm and filled in with screed

100 mm oversite concrete

provide deep timber joists spanning over the full width, the ends carried on galvanised steel joist hangers built into the inner leaf of the wall (21.06).

21.05

Sometimes a timber floor is required to be provided on a solid base such as the oversite concrete. This floor may be provided by means of wood blocks and these are usually bedded direct onto a hot bitumen dpc immediately over the screeded concrete.

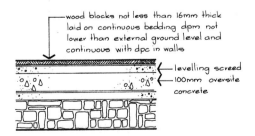

wood blocks not less than 16mm thick laid on continuous bedding dpm not lower than external ground level and continuous with dpc in walls

levelling screed

100mm oversite concrete

Another method which provides a satisfactory fixing for softwood or hardwood boarding is to place splayed timber fillets onto a hot bitumen dpc

and fill in around them with a fine concrete mix. The boarding may then be nailed down to the fillets.

The fillets must be impregnated as described before (21.02) and care must be taken to see that the dpc is continuous with that provided in the adjoining walls.

21.06

The construction of upper floors of suspended timber is somewhat different from that of ground floors. In the first place there are no sleeper walls to break the spans and timbers must span between walls or supports. Consequently they are deeper and often placed closer together to carry the loads imposed on them.

Although at one time timber joists were built into external walls this practice is now no longer used unless the ends of the hoists are protected by wrapping them in building paper or sheet polythene. Exposure of the end of the joist into the cavity is not good practice, except when the ends of the joist are stepped in an organic based preservative.

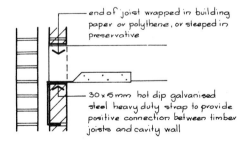

end of joist wrapped in building paper or polythene, or sleeped in preservative

30 x 5 mm hot dip galvanised steel heavy duty strap to provide positive connection between timber joists and cavity wall

A better method is to build into the inner leaf of the cavity wall a galvanised pressed steel joist hanger into which the end of the joist can be placed and secured by nailing through the side. The load applied on the wall is thus purely vertical and any upward thrust from the joist end under deflection is within the internal void of the building.

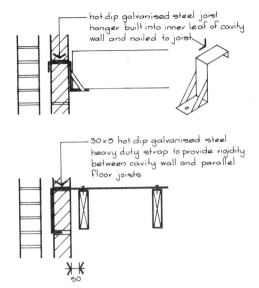

When joists run parallel with an external wall they should be set about 50 mm from the face.

21.07

Upper floors over about 2.5 m span tend to vibrate underfoot. To increase their stability the joists are strutted at centre span at intervals not exceeding 2 m. This is known as herringbone strutting and greatly increases the rigidity of the floor. Care must be taken to securely wedge the end joist off the wall.

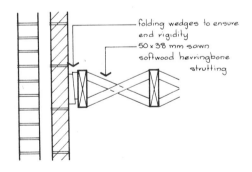

Pressed steel bracketing is now available which fulfills the same purpose.

Solid strutting is more normal in Scotland. The struts would be sawn boards 25 mm thick with a depth approx. 25 mm less than the joist depth.

21.08

The size and spacing of timber floor joists depends on the span and floor loading. In general, centres are either 400, 450 or 600 mm which conform to the widths or fixing centres of plasterboard or lath for the ceiling or particle board for the flooring. Joists are invariably 50 mm thick which allows sufficient surface for nailing abutting board. The sizes and centres of floor joists for domestic structures are precisely defined in the Building Regulations Schedule 6 Table 1*. As a rough guide the empirical method of calculating the depth of joist is as follows:

$$\frac{\text{span (mm)}}{24} \quad + 50 \quad \text{(at 400 mm centres)}$$

21.09

Two materials are in general use for finishing suspended timber floors:

(i) 19 mm thick flooring grade particle board (chipboard) with rebated joints provided with a specially compacted and sealed upper surface in boards of 1200 x 600 mm. This material is quick to lay being secured with round lost head nails and can be finished with a clear polyurethane lacquer to seal the surface. Care must be taken to ensure that the joists are set at precisely the correct centres as longitudinal joints must be supported.

(ii) Prepared (wrot) tongued and grooved softwood boarding to BS 1297:1970, in the following dimensions:

Finished thickness (mm)	19	19	21	28
Finished width on face (mm)	65	90	113	137

As timber is a natural material and prone to movement due to humidity changes, boards tend to curl and twist while in the stack. Narrow boards are preferable as they show less tendency to distortion. Consequently to provide a level surface the boards must be cramped up tightly to ensure that the tongue and grooved joints are fully butting and that all twist or curl is flattened out. The boards are fixed by two 65 mm nails to every joist crossed, nails either being round lost heads or preferably steel cut brads. All heading joints between boards must occur over joists to ensure proper support and fixing.

The thickness of floorboard to span between joists is defined in the Building Regulations (D14, Schedule 6, Table 13*).

Finished thickness (mm)	Max. span (mm)
16	505
19	600
21	635
28	790

21.10

All floors should be cleaned off with a plane or sander to remove rough patches and high points and then properly protected from damage, plaster and paint splashes. A minimum protection is a thick coat of sawdust but if hardwood blocks or boarding are laid these should be covered up with insulation board or a similar material.

22.00 Roof construction

The roof of a building is a primary element of enclosure, exercising a dominant effect on the design as a whole. It has dual functions:

(i) to keep out the weather, and

(ii) to keep in the warmth.

As the roof is the most exposed element of a building the satisfactory solution of its aesthetic and functional requirements are fundamental to a successful total performance of the whole superstructure. The supporting structure and the roof are regarded as basic permanent elements which must be designed and constructed to last without excessive maintenance for the anticipated life of the building.

Bearing in mind that the roof is more vulnerable to the effects of atmospheric pollution, solar radiation, heat loss to cold clear skies (irradiation) and the action of rain, it is as well to remember that the pitched roof weathered with the traditional materials of slate or tiles has proved itself over many hundred of years.

The technical and constructional problems of flat roof design have not yet been successfully overcome. Water penetration, condensation and moisture entrapped during construction are still formidable problems.

22.01

All roof structures must be designed to:

(i) Provide adequate resistance to failure by overloading or overstressing;

(ii) Accommodate dimensional changes due to movement of the superstructure caused by drying out of construction water or thermal expansion;

(iii) Reduce structural movement of its own members to acceptable limits

Roof structures must therefore be capable of carrying the loads imposed upon them, take up movement in the superstructure caused by heat or drying out and be so constructed that the members of the

roof are not only rigid under load but their joints are strong enough to withstand imposed stresses without movement.

The loads imposed on a roof structure are as follows:

(i) The dead load of the structure and weathering.

(ii) Imposed loads which depend on the angle of pitch.

(iii) Loads imposed on the outer roof surface by wind pressure or eddying (CP 3 Chapter V, Pt. (i) and Building Regulations D2)*.

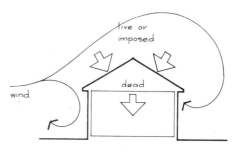

Loadings imposed on roof structure

The sizes of timbers for domestic structures conforming to the above requirements are included in the 'deemed to satisfy' provisions of the Building Regulations D14, Schedules 6 and 10*.

22.02

The pitch of the roof is defined in BS 3589:1963 *Glossary of building terms* as follows:

Flat.   Angle to the horizontal not exceeding 10°.

Pitched.   Angle to the horizontal exceeding 10° but not exceeding 70° (thereafter a wall).

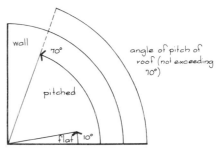

Definition and limitation of angles of roof pitch (BS 3589)

22.03

The pitch of a roof is determined by the material used for weathering the upper surface, the principal objective being to throw off rainwater as quickly as possible. Basically, the smaller the unit size of the covering material the steeper the pitch. If the pitch is too shallow there is a tendency for water to make its way by capillary attraction up the slope between the weathering units and find its way through the joints. This problem is most common in slating and single lap tiles.

Generally, the lower the angle of pitch the greater the angle of water spread.

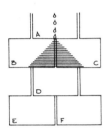

water runs off slate A into joint between B and C, spreading between underside of these and slate D. If pitch is too shallow this water can be blown or drawn up by capillary attraction over heads of slates E and F

Problem of water creep in slate roofing – the flatter the pitch, the greater the angle of creep

The minimum angle of pitch to be used for various common coverings to pitched roofs is as follows:

(i) Hand-made clay plain tiles   45°
    (265 x 165 mm)

(ii) Machine-made clay plain tiles   35°
    (265 x 165 mm)

(iii) Concrete plain tiles   35°
    (265 x 165 mm)

(iv) Concrete or clay pantiles   35°
    (single lap tiles – 420 x 280 mm)

(v) Patent concrete interlocking tiles   22½°
    (various sizes generally about 430 x 380 mm)

(vi) Slates (natural)   25°
    'Ladies' size.   400 x 200 mm.
    'Countesses'.   500 x 250 mm.
    'Duchesses'.   600 x 300 mm.

22.04

The construction of traditional pitched roof structures is carried out under the following principles:

(i) The timber used conforms in all respects to CP 112 and BS 2978:1973 (21.01)

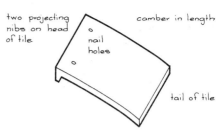

two projecting nibs on head of tile   camber in length   nail holes   tail of tile

Handmade clay plain tile - thickness 10mm

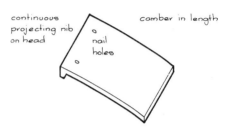

continuous projecting nib on head   camber in length   nail holes

Machine-made clay plain tile - thickness 10mm

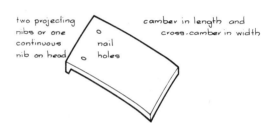

two projecting nibs or one continuous nib on head   camber in length and cross-camber in width   nail holes

Concrete plain tile - thickness 10mm

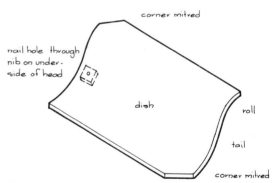

corner mitred   nail hole through nib on underside of head   dish   roll   tail   corner mitred

Pantile - thickness 10mm approx.

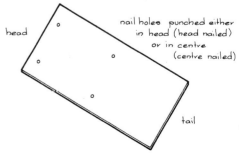

head   nail holes punched either in head (head nailed) or in centre (centre nailed)   tail

Natural slate - thickness 6mm approx.

(ii) The various members of the structure are cut, fitted and assembled using sound traditional jointing techniques and securely nailed or fixed by other approved means.

The basic members forming a simple pitched roof structure are shown in the following sketch:

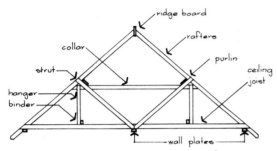

Basic members forming simple traditional roof structure

In addition, when the roof is required to be constructed over an L-shaped building it may be necessary to construct the roof with internal and external angles to the slopes. Internal angles are called 'valleys' and external angles are called 'hips'.

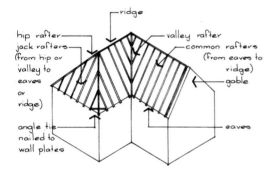

The angles are formed from 25 mm thick sawn boards with a depth of at least 200 mm set at the

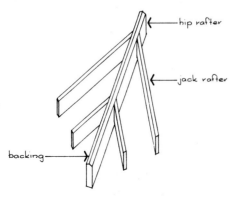

Sketch showing connection of jack rafters to hip rafter

correct angle from eaves to ridgeboard against which the rafters are cut to an angle to sit closely and are then securely nailed to the hip or valley rafter.

In addition a 100 x 50 mm sawn angle tie is provided across the angle under the hip rafter about 1.5 m long, securely nailed to the wall plate to prevent this spreading on the wall due to thrust from the hip rafter.

22.05
There are two main types of traditional timber pitched roof in common use today. All dimensions shown are illustrative only.

(i) *Single roof* spanning from 3—5 m and varying in construction to suit the purpose of the design.

(a) *Lean-to roof* for single storey addition abutting two or more stories, maximum span 3 m.

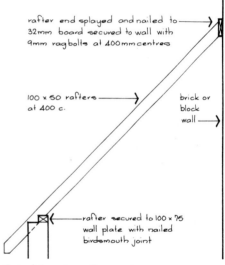

Typical lean-to roof - maximum span 3m

(b) *Couple roof* for a situation where maximum headroom is required, maximum span 4 m.

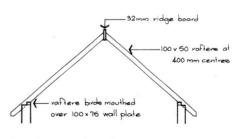

Typical couple roof - maximum span 4m

(c) *Close couple roof* maximum span 5 m. The ceiling joist helps to prevent the roof spreading.

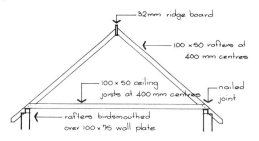

Typical close couple roof - maximum span 5m

(d) *Collar roof*, a variation of the close couple roof where extra headroom is required, maximum span 5 m.

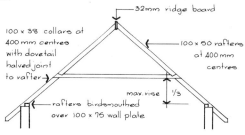

Typical collar roof - maximum span 5m

The joints of these roofs are an important part of their strength and are shown in detail as follows:

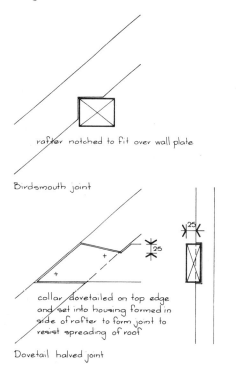

Birdsmouth joint

Dovetail halved joint

(ii) Double roofs which incorporate a longitudinal timber called a purlin whose purpose is to reduce the span of the rafter and thus reduce the size of timber required. The purlin is itself supported at intervals of about 2.4 m by a strut bearing onto a binder (which 'binds' ceiling rafters and struts together) and by a horizontal tie (collar) which supports the underside of the purlin and helps to prevent the roof spreading under load. There are a number of variations to this construction, of which the following is an example:

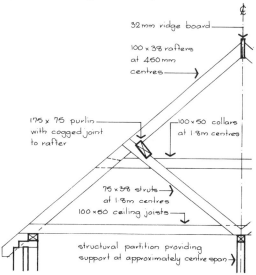

Typical double roof with struts supported on loadbearing partition

The details of the jointing to strut, purlin, binder and collar are important and are generally as follows:

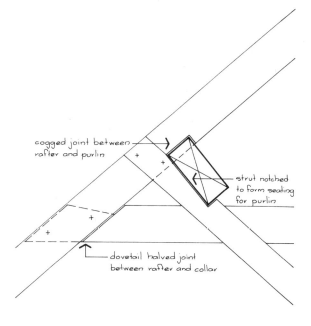

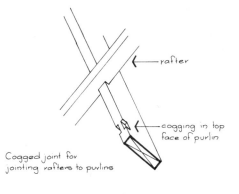

Cogged joint for jointing rafters to purlins

— rafter

— cogging in top face of purlin

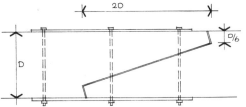

Splayed scarfed joint for jointing purlins in length — also used for jointing ridge boards, but bolts and straps replaced by long nails and length of joint reduced to 1½ D

22.06

In addition, there are two forms of timber roof construction called trussed rafters or timber trusses which are used for domestic buildings which employ timber connectors to secure the timbers instead of traditional jointing.

(i) The *two-sided toothed plate connector* of 75 mm diameter is pressed from thin galvanised steel sheet and after being placed between the two timbers to be connected, is secured by a 12 mm dia bolt with 50 mm galvanised sheet steel square washers under head and nut. This connector forms the principal jointing medium of timber trusses spanning up to 11 m at 1.8 m centres. An example of this is shown in the illustration.

(ii) The *galvanised steel plate* with sharp projecting tangs of varying sizes to suit particular applications and applied to both sides of the butt jointed timbers and pressed into the fibres by hydraulic pressure or nailed with thread rolled nails.

The trussed rafters produced with the aid of these gang nail plates are supplied and delivered to site by specialist fabricators and usually designed for the specific span and loads of the contract. Fixed at 600 mm centres they require a wall plate but no purlins or ridge board, lateral stability being provided by the tiling battens on which the tiles are hung. These rafters span up to 8 m and pitches from 10 to 25°.

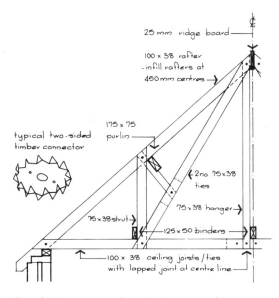

typical two-sided timber connector

25 mm ridge board

100 × 38 rafter -infill rafters at 450mm centres

175 × 75 purlin

2 no. 75 × 38 ties

75 × 38 hanger

75 × 38 strut

125 × 50 binders

100 × 38 ceiling joists / ties with lapped joint at centre line

Typical timber truss utilising toothed timber plate connectors for spans up to 11m

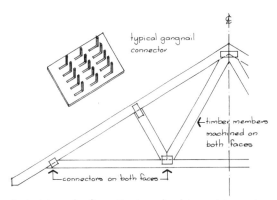

typical gangnail connector

timber members machined on both faces

connectors on both faces

Typical trussed rafter with sherardised truss plate joints for spans up to 11m

22.07

In terrace housing the provision of loadbearing cross walls at regular centres lends itself to the employment of a roof construction based on a timber construction called the trussed purlin. Here, instead of a separate purlin, struts and binders, a timber lattice beam with joints based on the use of gang nail plates is fabricated to carry the direct loads of the rafters bearing on the top surface and the ceiling joists securely nailed up to the bottom member of the truss. These trussed purlins are designed and supplied by specialist fabricators.

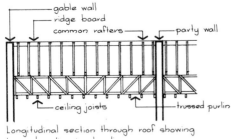

Longitudinal section through roof showing trussed purlins in elevation

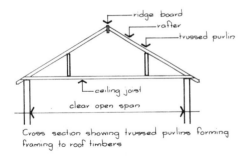

Cross section showing trussed purlins forming framing to roof timbers

22.08

Pitched roofs weathered with tiles or slates need to be sealed from driving rain or snow finding its way through the joints. To effect this an untearable sarking felt with a hessian base conforming to BS 747 Pt. 2:1968 is fixed to the top surface of the rafters. As the width of the felt necessitates jointing, this is formed by commencing laying at the eaves and lapping the upper layers over the lower by at least 75 mm. Vertical joints are made over rafters where the felt should lap at least 150 mm. The addition of an aluminium foil to the sarking felt greatly increases the insulation of the roof at little extra cost. The felt must be dressed up over the ridge board, over the gable ends and the fascia board, in the latter case to extend 50 mm proud of the fascia to allow any water collected to drain into the eaves gutter.

Where the roof slopes incorporate valleys and hips

an extra full width layer is fixed under the felt to ensure proper sealing. The felt is fixed with 32 x 2.5 mm aluminium or galvanised iron clout head nails at 300 mm centres.

22.09

Tiles and slates are hung or fixed to sawn softwood battens nailed to the rafters through the sarking felt. The size of the battens used depends on

(i) the type and weight of slate or tile used, and

(ii) the spacing of the rafters.

A guide for the size of sawn timber battens is as follows:

Roofing material	Spacing of rafters	
	(450 mm)	(600 mm)
Tiles: plain	25 x 20	30 x 25
pantiles	40 x 20	40 x 25
single lap (interlocking)	40 x 20	40 x 25
Slates: natural	40 x 20	40 x 25

Tile and slating battens should be impregnated against rot in accordance with BS 4072: 1974 (21.02) and fixed with galvanised iron, aluminium or composition nails.

22.10

There are a number of terms applicable to tiling and slating as follows:

(i) The 'margin' which is the amount of the slate or tile which is exposed on the roof surface.

(ii) the 'lap' which is the amount by which alternate courses of slates or tiles cover each other at the ends. These are generally as follows:

(a) Plain tiles	65 mm (double lap)
(b) Pantiles	75 mm (single lap)
(c) Natural slates	75/150 mm (double lap)

(iii) The 'gauge' which is the distance tail to tail at which the slates or tiles are set — this is also the centres of fixing battens

(a) The gauge for plain and pantiles is calculated as follows:

$$\text{Gauge} = \frac{\text{length of tile} - \text{lap}}{2} \quad \text{(mm)}$$

(b) The gauge for slating depends whether the slates are head or centre nailed. Longer slates are generally centre nailed to prevent wind lift and snapping but this method is not so satisfactory as head nailing as the hole piercing the slate is relatively close to the tail of the slate.

Head nailing

$$\text{Gauge} = \frac{\text{length of slate} - (\text{lap} - 25)}{2}$$

Centre nailing

$$\text{Gauge} = \frac{\text{length of slate} - \text{lap (mm)}}{2}$$

A guide to the correct gauge for various types of tye tiles and slates is as follows:

Type of roofing unit	Size of tile/slate (mm)	Gauge of battens (mm)
Plain clay/concrete tile	265 x 165	100
Pantile	420 x 280	343
Interlocking concrete tile	430 x 380	355
	610 x 356	265(25°)
	500 x 250	220(30°)
Natural slate	500 x 250	214(25°)
	600 x 300	265(25°)

22.11

The eaves of pitched roofs always incorporate a double course of roofing tiles or slates to seal the vertical

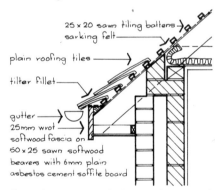

Typical eaves detail showing fascia and cavity closure

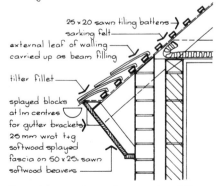

Typical eaves detail showing splayed fascia and through cavity detail

joint in the lowest course except interlocking tiles which have no need of this.

All slates are nailed every course throughout the roof. Tiled roofs are nailed two courses at ridge and eaves and two tiles out from verges. Plain tiles are nailed every fourth course throughout the roof. Nails are either aluminium or composition.

22.12

At the edge of the roof over a bargeboard or gable wall the upper surface of the weathering is given a slight tilt inwards to throw rainwater away from the edge where it would drop.

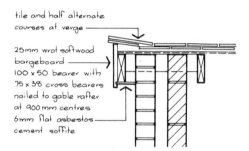

Typical verge detail incorporating bargeboard

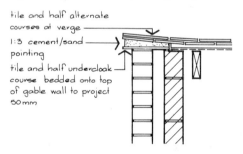

Typical verge detail to plain tile roof showing undercloak detail

An undercloak course is provided over the brick-work and the gap is bedded in cement and sand (1:3) and neatly sunk pointed. Alternate courses are made out with tile and half or slate and half to avoid the use of slip tiles or slates which would become dislodged in high winds at such an exposed position.

22.13

At the apex or 'ridge' of the pitched roof the open courses of tiling or slating are covered with a ridge tile which is bedded down in cement and sand (1:3)

with the joints neatly flush pointed. A variety of ridge tiles and slates are in use as follows:

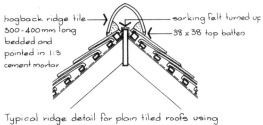

hogback ridge tile — 300 - 400 mm long bedded and pointed in 1:3 cement mortar

sarking felt turned up

38 x 38 top batten

Typical ridge detail for plain tiled roofs using hogback ridge tile

half round

angle

segmental

Alternative ridge tiles all 200 mm wide at base and minimum thickness of 16mm

The free ends of half round and hogback ridge tiles are filled in either with brick slips (tiled roofs) or bottle ends (slate roofs).

22.14

Hip angles either incorporate a special angle tile set in course with the plain tile on the roof or use a half round tile as used for the ridge.

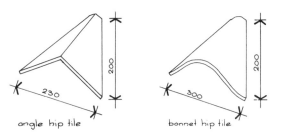

200

230

angle hip tile

200

300

bonnet hip tile

Hip angle tiles for setting in course with plain tile roofs

It is usual to fix a galvanised iron hip iron, securely screwed to the top edge of the hip rafter to prevent half round hip tiles becoming dislodged and sliding off the roof.

22.15

Valleys, when incorporated in plain tile roofs, are usually formed by purpose-made tapered valley tiles which are incorporated in the courses of tiles as these are laid.

With pantiles, interlocking tiles and slates, it is necessary to lay 300 mm wide 25 mm wrot softwood valley boards on either side of the valley and weather these with Code 4 lead including dressing the lead over softwood tilting fillets over which the tiles

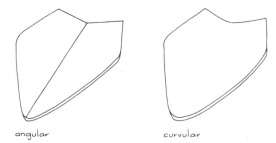

angular

curvular

Valley tiles for use with plain clay tile roofing

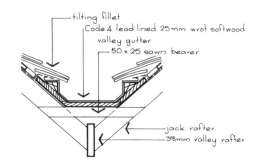

tilting fillet

Code 4 lead lined 25mm wrot softwood valley gutter

50 x 25 sawn bearer

jack rafter

38mm valley rafter

Detail of lead-lined valley gutter

project. The tiles or slates are neatly splay-cut down the angle of the valley and securely nailed to the battens on either side.

22.16

The Building Regulations (Part F)* require that the roofs of domestic buildings are insulated. A number of approved materials are specified (F4 Schedule 11)* among which, for timber pitched roofs finished with tiles or slates, are the following materials:

Exfoliated loose fill vermiculite	70 mm thick
Mineral fibre quilt	46 mm thick
Expanded polystyrene insulating board	38 mm thick

The inclusion of a foil-backed sarking felt reduces the required thickness.

Low pitched roofs (below 22½°) do not contain a sufficient volume of air to absorb the volume of water vapour rising through the ceiling from the rooms below and consequently condensation occurs on the underside of the cold sarking felt. To remove this problem ceilings of low pitched roofs should be provided with a vapour barrier as described earlier (16.09) immediately on the underside of the insulation. In addition vents must be provided through the eaves to provide cross ventilation. A minimum of 300 sq. mm/300 mm run of eaves is required, i.e. a 15 mm dia hole every 300 mm run of eaves.

22.17

Flat roofs, i.e. those with a pitch below 10° to the horizontal, are constructed in a similar manner to floors, whether using timber or reinforced concrete as the structural medium. In addition, they have similar problems and functions as pitched roofs in respect of:

(i) The need for structural stability.

(ii) The need to remove rainwater as quickly as possible.

(iii) The need to provide a durable weatherproof finish.

(iv) The need to conserve heat within the structure and to prevent excess heat or cold passing through into the interior.

(v) The need to prevent interstitial condensation.

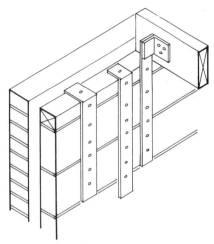

Examples of sherardised pressed steel straps for securing wall plates and timber joists to prevent lifting by wind suction over flat roofs

22.18

Structural stability is ensured by designing the structure in accordance with the requirements previously described (22.01). The Building Regulations do, however, provide 'deemed to satisfy' provisions for the construction of flat timber roofs. These provisions, in the form of tables (D14 Schedule 6)*, relate to the following:

(i) Timbers which are
   (a) Stress graded SS and MSS.
   (b) Not graded.

(ii) Roof deck joists where access is for maintenance and repair only

(iii) Roof deck joists where access is *not* limited to maintenance and repair only.

The joist sizes shown in the examples are illustrative only.

Timber joists used for flat roof construction must be bedded down to the wall below with galvanised mild steel straps to prevent wind suction lifting the roof unless a parapet is provided to hold the structure down. In addition stability often requires the addition of herringbone strutting as described before for timber first floor construction on (21.08).

22.19

The need to remove rainwater as quickly as possible from flat or low pitched roofs is a prime requirement. Excessive build up of water may well cause loadings in excess of the design criteria. It is not possible to produce a perfectly flat roof surface except by such means and care as to make the cost exorbitant. 'Flat' surfaces therefore include high and low points and when these areas are covered with water ponding will occur in the low spots.

If the roof is always covered with water, this will act as an insulant and keep the weathering membrane cool. When ponding occurs, the area of membrane under the water remains cooler than dry areas open to the sun's rays. Grit or spar finishes have little effect in reducing this. The warmer areas of roof expand and stresses occur in the membrane around the perimeter of the ponding which, in the case of many bituminous felt roofing materials, can eventually cause failure by splitting or tearing. The roof then fails as a weathering element.

It is therefore imperative to remove rainwater and this is effected by sloping the surface of the flat roof element. This can be accomplished in two ways:

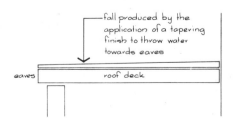

fall produced by the application of a tapering finish to throw water towards eaves

eaves   roof deck

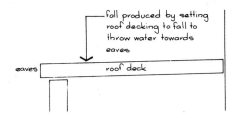

fall produced by setting roof decking to fall to throw water towards eaves

eaves

roof deck

The minimum fall to which a flat roof should be constructed is 1 in 60.

22.20

The problem of insulation to flat roofs can be dealt with in two ways, either:

(i) by providing the insulation on top of the supporting timber joists or concrete slab, or

(ii) by providing the insulation underneath.

With timber construction it is often economically advantageous to provide a decking which not only provides support for the weathering but also acts as the insulant required under the Building Regulations. Falls are produced by tapered timber slips called firrings.

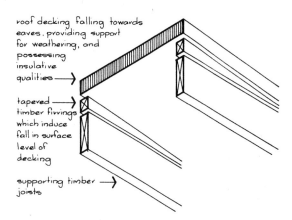

roof decking falling towards eaves, providing support for weathering, and possessing insulative qualities →

tapered timber firrings which induce fall in surface level of decking →

supporting timber joists →

Typical insulated roof decking set to fall on firrings supported by timber joists

Concrete decks often use a lightweight cement screed to produce both fall and insulation. The screeds include either an air entraining agent to produce air filled voids or lightweight aggregate such as exfoliated vermiculite or foamed slag. Wet screeds have a tendency to take some time to dry out and thus water can be trapped under the applied weathering coat which will in time form blisters. Small vents can be incorporated in the weathering to relieve this pressure.

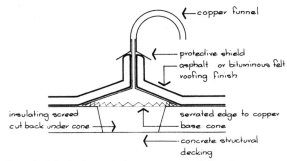

← copper funnel

← protective shield

← asphalt or bituminous felt roofing finish

insulating screed cut back under cone →

serrated edge to copper base cone

← concrete structural decking

Detail of typical proprietary pressure relief vent

In addition the varying thickness of these insulating screeds can cause variations in thermal conductivity in the structure forming 'cold spots' and sometimes condensation at these points. In addition vapour barriers must be incorporated as discussed earlier earlier (22.15).

Probably the best solution is to produce the falls either by inclining the slab or beam or providing firrings or sloping screeds and insulating the roof and weathering in one operation by incorporation of the necessary insulation within the weathering structure, the underlay forming the vapour barrier.

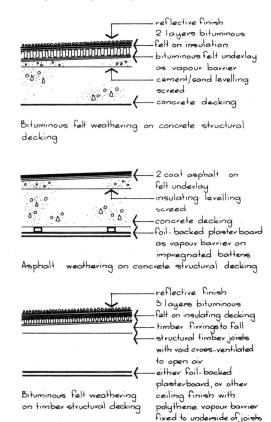

reflective finish 2 layers bituminous felt on insulation

bituminous felt underlay as vapour barrier

cement/sand levelling screed

concrete decking

Bituminous felt weathering on concrete structural decking

2 coat asphalt on felt underlay

insulating levelling screed

concrete decking

foil-backed plasterboard as vapour barrier on impregnated battens

Asphalt weathering on concrete structural decking

reflective finish 3 layers bituminous felt on insulating decking

timber firrings to fall

structural timber joists with void cross-ventilated to open air

either foil-backed plasterboard, or other ceiling finish with polythene vapour barrier fixed to underside of joists

Bituminous felt weathering on timber structural decking

Some examples of roof construction illustrating positioning of insulation and vapour barrier

The void in the timber roof formed by the depth of the timber joist must be cross ventilated as described before (22.15).

22.21

The structural upper surface of timber flat roofs can be formed from a number of materials. These, apart from timber boarding, are all sheet materials and care must be taken to ensure:

(i) The centres of the supporting joists coincide with standard widths of sheet and that intermediate joists conform to centres recommended by the manufacturers.

(ii) The joists are sufficiently wide to enable the edges of the sheets to be properly nailed down to them (50 mm is the minimum).

(iii) The ends of sheets are supported on bearers to avoid sagging under load.

Materials used for decking include:

25 mm prepared tongued and grooved softwood boarding which should be treated with preservative.

50 mm woodwool slabs.

19 mm particle board (chipboard) flooring grade.

9 mm WBP (water and boil proof) grade plywood to BS 1455.

22.22

The verges, eaves and abutment details of timber flat roofs incorporate particular features which are indicated in the following examples:

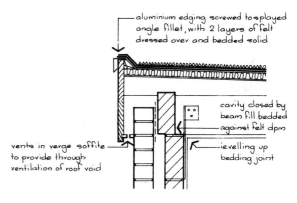

Verge detail

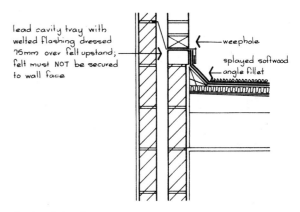

Abutment detail

Typical details incorporating insulated decking over bitumen felt vapour barrier

22.23

Concrete flat roofs to small domestic structures are usually formed from *in situ* concrete either cast onto fully continuous supported ply decked shuttering the concrete reinforced by the insertion of mild steel bars or fabric in the bottom of the slab with a minimum cover of 25 mm (19.07), or by casting the concrete onto a mesh of expanded metal lathing incorporating steel U ribs for strength forming a permanent

Eaves detail

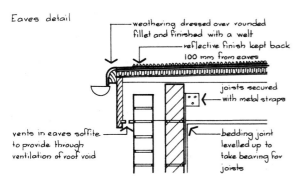

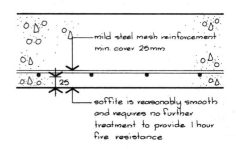

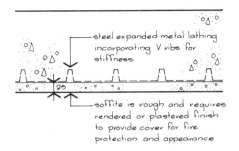

steel expanded metal lathing incorporating V ribs for stiffness

25

soffite is rough and requires rendered or plastered finish to provide cover for fire protection and appearance

combined shutter and reinforcement. This is temporarily supported until the concrete has gained its designed strength (at 28 days) by expanding steel props and timber bearers. The soffite of the expanded metal reinforcement requires the addition of 25 mm gypsum plaster applied in two coats to provide the necessary fire resistance.

22.24
The verge, eaves and abutment details of reinforced concrete flat roofs incorporate particular features indicated in the following examples:

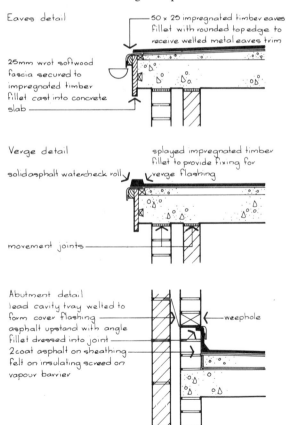

Eaves detail

50 x 25 impregnated timber eaves fillet with rounded top edge to receive welted metal eaves trim

25mm wrot softwood fascia secured to impregnated timber fillet cast into concrete slab

Verge detail

splayed impregnated timber fillet to provide fixing for verge flashing

solid asphalt watercheck roll

movement joints

Abutment detail
lead cavity tray welted to form cover flashing
asphalt upstand with angle fillet dressed into joint
2 coat asphalt on sheathing felt on insulating screed on vapour barrier

weephole

Typical details of reinforced concrete roof with insulating screed and weathered with 2 coats asphalt

22.25
Two materials are in general use for the weathering of flat roofs for domestic buildings:

(i) Three layer bitumen felt roofing to CP 144 Pt. 3: 1970 and BS 747:1968, laid with 50 mm side laps, 75 mm end laps, all staggered. The layers bonded together in hot bitumen and finished with a surface of 10 mm white spar chippings bedded in hot bitumen to act as a solar reflective.

(ii) Two layers of asphalt to CP 114 Pt. 4L 1970, of total thickness of 20 mm, on black sheathing felt underlay, with laps not less than 150 mm and the final layer finished with sharp sand and either a white bitumen solar reflective coat or 300 x 300 x 8 mm asbestos cement tiles bedded in hot bitumen.

Both materials rely on the stability of the supporting structure without which they have a tendency to crack and fail as a weathering agent. Other materials in use include lead, copper and aluminium sheet.

22.26
The removal of rainwater can be effected in three ways either:

(i) by providing at the eaves or low points of flat roofs, gutters of either metal, asbestos cement or plastic. From outlets in the bottom of the gutter, water passes through rainwater pipes into the storm-water chains at the foot of the wall, or

(ii) by forming falls to flat roofs and inserting at the lowest point a rainwater outlet which is securely sealed to the weathering membrane. This discharges into a vertical rainwater pipe which, passing down through the structure discharges into the stormwater drains at ground floor level, or

(iii) by collection through parapet walls into hopper heads.

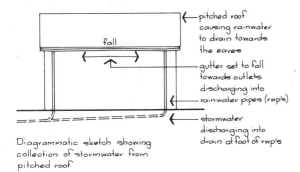

pitched roof causing rainwater to drain towards the eaves

gutter set to fall towards outlets discharging into rainwater pipes (rwp's)

stormwater discharging into drain at foot of rwp's

Diagrammatic sketch showing collection of stormwater from pitched roof

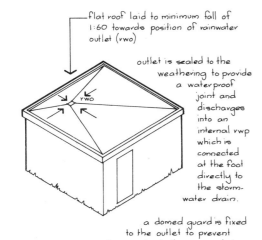

flat roof laid to minimum fall of 1:60 towards position of rainwater outlet (rwo)

outlet is sealed to the weathering to provide a waterproof joint and discharges into an internal rwp which is connected at the foot directly to the stormwater drain.

a domed guard is fixed to the outlet to prevent leaves, etc., in the rwp or drain

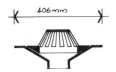

406 mm

Typical uPVC domed roof outlet

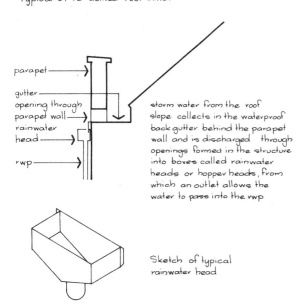

parapet

gutter

opening through parapet wall

rainwater head

rwp

storm water from the roof slope collects in the waterproof back gutter behind the parapet wall and is discharged through openings formed in the structure into boxes called rainwater heads or hopper heads, from which an outlet allows the water to pass into the rwp

Sketch of typical rainwater head

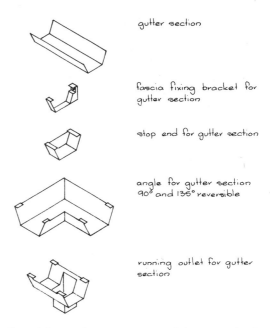

gutter section

fascia fixing bracket for gutter section

stop end for gutter section

angle for gutter section 90° and 135° reversible

running outlet for gutter section

Typical fittings for eaves gutter installation; example shown is for square section gutter in PVC - similar fittings available to suit half round and ogee gutters in asbestos cement, cast iron, aluminium, pressed steel and PVC

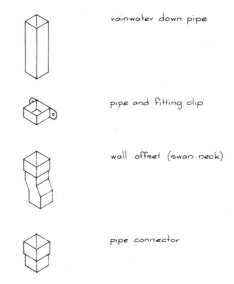

rainwater down pipe

pipe and fitting clip

wall offset (swan-neck)

pipe connector

Typical fittings for rainwater down pipe installation; example shown is square section rwp in PVC - similar fittings available to suit round pipes in asbestos cement, cast iron, aluminium, pressed steel and PVC

22.27

Rainwater gutters are either rectangular, semi-circular or ogee in section. They are either fixed to the fascia by means of brackets or screwed direct (ogee pattern). Care must be taken to ensure that the sarking felt projects over the edge of the gutter. The ends of the gutter are sealed with stop ends and angles are available to take the gutter around the corners of the eaves. Outlet sections are available to discharge the flow of water into the rainwater pipe.

22.28

Rainwater pipes match the gutters in material and design. The pipes are fixed to the wall either by integral brackets or loose bracket fixings and double offset (swan neck) pipes allow connection between the gutter outlet on the projecting eaves and the pipe fixed to the wall below. Rain water pipes are either connected direct to the socket of the stormwater drain pipe or to back inlets provided to gullies.

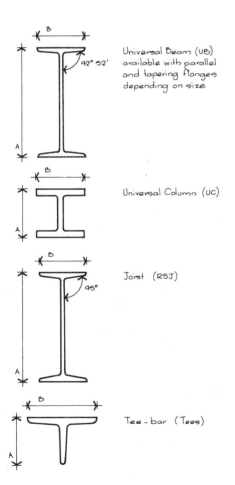

Universal Beam (UB) available with parallel and tapering flanges depending on size

Universal Column (UC)

Joist (RSJ)

Tee-bar (Tees)

23.00 Low rise steel frames

The design of structural steelwork is generally carried out by a structural engineer who, working from the architect's design drawings, prepares the steelwork design drawings, from which, with the aid of detail shop drawings, the steelwork is fabricated. The design and fabrication is carried out in accordance with BS 449 Pt. 2:1969 *The use of structural steel in buildings*. This is a 'deemed to satisfy' provision of the Building Regulations.

Structural steel of British manufacture is marked during rolling with the name or trade mark of the manufacturer. This implies compliance with BS 4 Pt. 1: 1972 *Hot rolled sections* and BS 4 Pt. 2:1969 *Hot rolled hollow sections*, and that the steel is of the strength designated as mild steel, generally used for small steel structures.

23.01

Structural steel is rolled from hot material to various profiles found to be useful in the construction of steel frames for buildings. These profiles are manufactured in a wide range of different sizes to enable the designer to select that required to comply with his theoretical design calculations and also to meet practical constructional requirements. The following table shows the range of profiles and sizes available:

	Size (mm)
Universal beams (UB)	914 x 419 (max)
	203 x 133 (min)
Universal columns (UC)	356 x 406 (max)
	152 x 152 (min)
Steel joists (RSJ)	203 x 102 (max)
	76 x 51 (min)
Tee-bars (tees)	152 x 152 (max)
	38 x 38 (min)
Channels (RSC)	432 x 102 (max)
	76 x 38 (min)
Equal angles (L)	203 x 203 (max)
	26 x 24 (min)
Unequal angles (L)	229 x 102 (max)
	51 x 38 (min)
Rectangular hollow sections (RHS)	152 x 76 (max)
	50 x 25 (min)
Square hollow sections (SHS)	355 x 355 (max)
	25 x 25 (min)

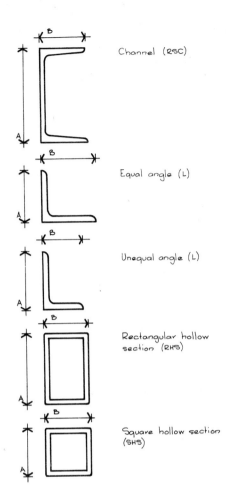

Channel (RSC)

Equal angle (L)

Unequal angle (L)

Rectangular hollow section (RHS)

Square hollow section (SHS)

In addition to these, there are a number of sections formed by cutting down standard rolled sections for particular uses. There are also hollow tube sections for specialist tubular fabrications in addition to mild steel plate which can be cut to shape and used for connections and strengthening where required.

23.02

Steel sections are secured together either

(i) by bolting them together with black mild steel or high tensile steel hexagonal bolts and nuts, or

(ii) by welding the members together, or

(iii) by rivetting in large structures.

Bolts are always used for site connections as the problems of site welding without proper jigging generally do not ensure a satisfactory job.

23.03

For small single-storey steel frames there are two basic designs in common use:

(i) The portal frame, which is a continuous structural member which follows the outline of the roof in shape, rigidly connected to the supporting posts to act as a complete frame structural unit. As the frames are bulky, delivery and erection is simplified by making the portals in a number of sections which are lifted and rigidly bolted together on site.

These steel portal structures are neat and simple internally allowing the full height to be used as no tie bars are required to reduce the available head height.

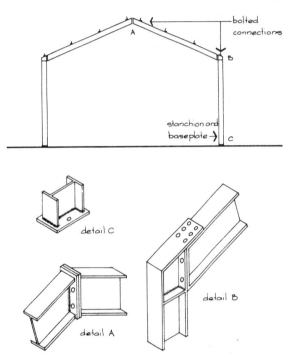

bolted connections

stanchion and baseplate →

detail C

detail B

detail A

Typical steel portal frame with frame and connection details

(ii) A simple post and truss arrangement which has the advantage of low cost. The trusses are bolted to a plate fixed to the top of the post and, as with portal frames, lateral stability is ensured by steel angle purlins with diagonal bracing in end bays to withstand wind loading.

(iii) Lattice beam and post which has the advantage of providing wide spans with relative economy.

In all these examples the positioning of the purlins is to meet the requirements of the type of roof sheeting or decking employed. The manufacturers of these stipulate purlin centres which must not be exceeded.

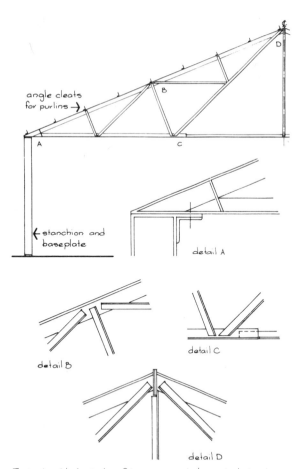

angle cleats
for purlins →

← stanchion and
baseplate

detail A

detail B

detail C

detail D

Typical welded steel roof truss, supported on steel stanchions, and frame connection details

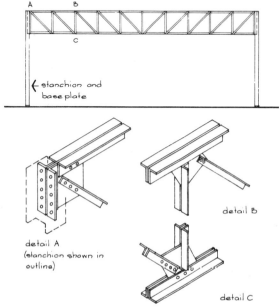

← stanchion and
base plate

detail A
(stanchion shown in outline)

detail B

detail C

Typical steel lattice beam roof truss, supported on web of steel stanchion, with frame connection details

23.04

Two-and three-storey buildings can be constructed with a steel frame which generally is extremely simple in design and fabrication. Stanchions for two-storey buildings are usually in single lengths but over this height a joint by means of a fishplate connection above the second floor level is used.

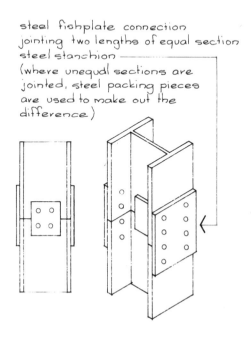

steel fishplate connection jointing two lengths of equal section steel stanchion ——————
(where unequal sections are jointed, steel packing pieces are used to make out the difference)

When the floors are of timber or precast concrete beams it is usual to provide a mild steel ledger angle bolted on either side of the beam web on which the ends of the joists or beams can rest.

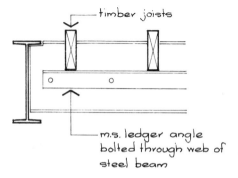

timber joists

m.s. ledger angle bolted through web of steel beam

In situ reinforced concrete floor can be cast between similar angles or resting wholly on top of the joist when mild steel studs are welded on to provide sheer connectors.

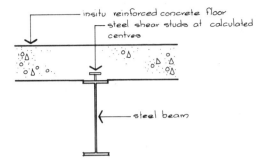

- insitu reinforced concrete floor
- steel shear studs at calculated centres
- steel beam

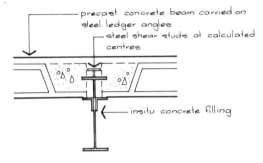

- precast concrete beam carried on steel ledger angles
- steel shear studs at calculated centres
- insitu concrete filling

construction to provide the period of fire resistance is shown in Building Regulations E1 (5)* Schedule 8.

casing of 1:2:4 concrete (non-loadbearing) with light steel reinforcement weight 0.48 kg/m² spaced at 150mm crs.
thickness (t) - 50mm (4 hours)
25mm (2 hours)

casing vermiculite/gypsum or perlite/gypsum on metal lathing spaced 25mm from flanges of steel
thickness (t) - 44mm (4 hours)
19mm (2 hours)

casing of 4:1 mix vermiculite/cement slabs reinforced with wire mesh and with plaster skim coat finish
thickness (t) - 63mm (4 hours)
25mm (2 hours)

Alternative examples for the protection of steel stanchions satisfying Building Regulations E1(5) Schedule 8

23.05

Stanchions and portal frames require not only that the load on the end be transferred adequately to the concrete foundation but also that the frame shall be properly anchored down to avoid distortion and probable failure due to wind loading. It is usual to weld a 12 mm steel plate about 300 x 300 mm on to the end of the stanchion. Long bolts with mild steel plates about 75 mm square are set in mortices in the concrete (14.02) and the stanchion bases are wedged up to provide a gap of about 25 mm. This gap and the mortices in the concrete are grouted up with neat cement grout (14.03).

23.06

Fire resistance to structural steel frames is not required for single-storey buildings except when the steelwork forms part of a party wall between two separate occupations or the distance to the boundary of the site is less than that permitted under the Building Regulations (E5)* when 1 hour fire resistance for separating walls must be provided. This can be effected by casing the steel in 12 mm asbestos insulating board.

When a steel frame is provided for a building exceeding one storey in height it must be protected against fire for the notional period laid down in the Building Regulations (E5)*. The 'deemed to satisfy'

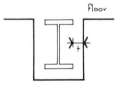

floor

casing of 1:2:4 concrete (non-loadbearing) with 23mm binding wire or steel mesh reinforcement weight 0.48 kg/m² spaced at 150mm centres
thickness (t) - 63mm (4 hours)
25mm (2 hours)

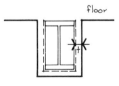

floor

casing of vermiculite/gypsum or perlite/gypsum on metal lathing spaced with void next to steel flanges
thickness (t) - 32mm (4 hours)
12.5mm (2 hours)

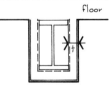

floor

casing of 4:1 mix vermiculite/cement slabs reinforced with wire mesh and with plaster skim coat finish
thickness (t) - 63mm (4 hours)
25mm (2 hours)

Alternative examples for the protection of steel beams satisfying Building Regulations E1(5) Schedule 8

23.07

Corrosion is a serious problem with all ferrous metals. Unless rust and scale are removed and a protective coating against further corrosion applied the life of the steelwork will be limited.

Rust and scale are removed by either wire brushing, the application of an acid neutralising solution or by means of air abrasives. The cleaned surface of the steel must then be immediately protected by the application of a metal primer; either red lead primer to BS 2523 or a zinc rich primer such as zinc chromate to BS 4652. Bearing surfaces of steelwork employing friction grip bolts must be left unprimed to ensure close contact between the steel surfaces.

23.08

A wide variety of materials including brick and block-work are used to clad steel frame structures. With cavity walling the principles enumerated earlier regarding stability, free and clear cavity and damp exclusion apply equally when the structural frame is of steel. Single storey steel structures are often clad with sheet materials to provide the weathering surface, insulation and an internal lining being added to the inside face. These materials include:

(i) Profiled asbestos cement sheeting, either natural finish or coloured.

'Major six' profile asbestos cement double cladding with insulation and underlining sheet

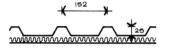

corrugated or troughed steel sheeting with insulated lining

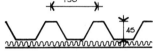

corrugated or troughed aluminium sheeting with insulated lining

(ii) Profiled steel sheet with a galvanised finish, faced externally with a coloured or textured plastic material.

(iii) Profiled aluminium sheet either natural colour finish, anodised to selected colours or faced with a coloured or textured plastic finish.

All these sheet materials have to conform to the fire requirements of the Building Regulations (E1)* and have a notional fire resistance of at least half-an-hour. This is usually provided by lining the interior of the sheeting with two thicknesses of 9.5 mm plaster-board.

Appendix: Building Standards (Scotland) Regulations 1971-1975

This Appendix lists the references to the Scottish Building Regulations which are indicated in the text by an asterisk.

The author and publishers gratefully acknowledge the help of Clifford Large, BA, MIOB, of the Glasgow College of Building and Printing, in compiling this appendix.

Explanatory Memoranda to Scottish Building Regulations are HMSO publications designed to serve as a guide to the Regulations. They must not be regarded as an authoritative interpretation of the Regulations.

Module A

Section 4.00   **Constraints and statutory controls in Scotland**

Prior to the 19th century control of building work was exercised by Dean of Guild Courts which only existed in Royal Burghs. By the middle of the century these powers had been extended to Parliamentary Burghs also. The first building regulations which were laid down for all burghs appeared in the Burgh Police Act 1892. The Public Health Act of 1897 gave county councils powers to make building bye-laws and the Burgh Police Act 1903 extended the same right to Burghs.

Model bye-laws were produced by the Department of Health for Scotland in the 1920's and these were revised in 1954. Local authorities were able to adopt or modify these bye-laws for their own use.

The first Building Regulations to apply to the whole of Scotland were the result of the Building (Scotland) Act 1959. These were the Building Standards (Scotland) Regulations 1963 which came into operation on 15 June 1964 and are the immediate forerunner of the Regulations now in force.

Section 4.04   The Building Standards (Scotland) Regulations which came into effect on June 15th 1964

Module B

Section 7.03   Load bearing sub-soils: no classification is given in Scottish Regulations.

Section 7.04   Scottish Regulations refer to compliance with CP 101

Section 8.03   The Highways Act 1959 does not apply in Scotland. The minimum distance to the face of a building (the building line) is given in the Burgh Police (Scotland) Act 1903 but local highway and planning authorities may require this distance to be increased.

Section 9.00   The Scottish equivalent is (A3) 'G5 Removal of Surface Soil and other matter'.

Module C

Section 11.06   B3/4 does not apply in Scotland. D14 is Schedule 10; C2 (2) Schedule 6 is Schedule 10, C2(2) (3) which refers to CP 112

Module D

Section 12.00 & Section 12.08   Schedule 10 G2 (1) refers to CP's 101 and 2004 which have similar requirements. Explanatory Memorandum Part C Table 1 gives minimum foundation sizes for different soils and foundation loadings.

Section 13.09   G7

Section 13.10   See 7.03.

Section 15.01   G6/G7

Module E

Section 16.01   C2(2)
               C1

Section 16.03   D5/6/7
     (ii)   D9
     (iii)   D18

Section 16.05   D5 and Schedule 9, Table 5
               Schedule 9, Tables 4 & 6
               All references to E5 are covered by D5.

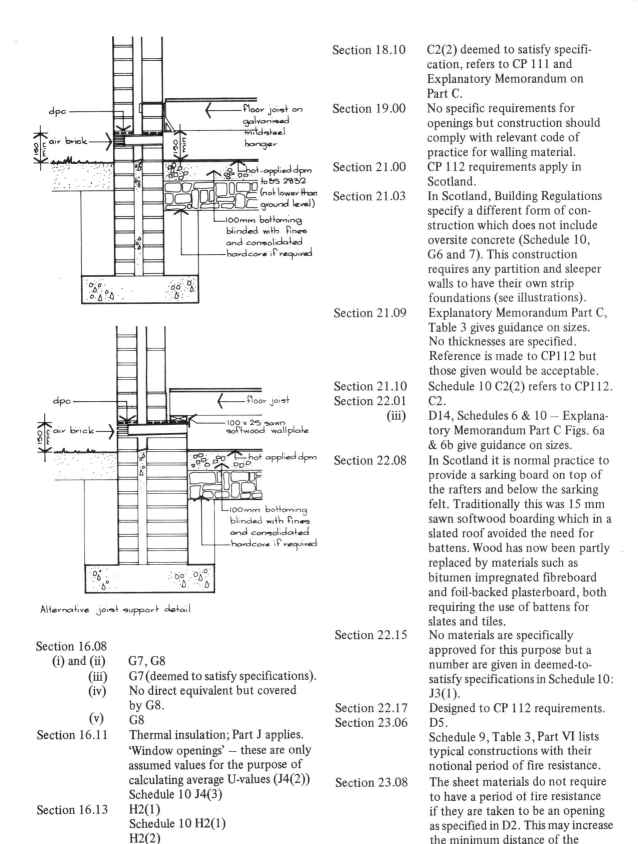

dpc

air brick

floor joist on
galvanised
mild steel
hanger

hot-applied dpm
to BS 2832
(not lower than
ground level)

100mm bottoming
blinded with fines
and consolidated
hardcore if required

dpc

air brick

floor joist

100 × 25 sawn
softwood wallplate

hot applied dpm

100mm bottoming
blinded with fines
and consolidated
hardcore if required

Alternative joist support detail

Section 16.08
(i) and (ii)   G7, G8
(iii)   G7 (deemed to satisfy specifications).
(iv)   No direct equivalent but covered
        by G8.
(v)   G8
Section 16.11   Thermal insulation; Part J applies.
        'Window openings' — these are only
        assumed values for the purpose of
        calculating average U-values (J4(2))
        Schedule 10 J4(3)
Section 16.13   H2(1)
        Schedule 10 H2(1)
        H2(2)
        Schedule 10 H2(2)

Section 18.10   C2(2) deemed to satisfy specifi-
        cation, refers to CP 111 and
        Explanatory Memorandum on
        Part C.
Section 19.00   No specific requirements for
        openings but construction should
        comply with relevant code of
        practice for walling material.
Section 21.00   CP 112 requirements apply in
        Scotland.
Section 21.03   In Scotland, Building Regulations
        specify a different form of con-
        struction which does not include
        oversite concrete (Schedule 10,
        G6 and 7). This construction
        requires any partition and sleeper
        walls to have their own strip
        foundations (see illustrations).
Section 21.09   Explanatory Memorandum Part C,
        Table 3 gives guidance on sizes.
        No thicknesses are specified.
        Reference is made to CP112 but
        those given would be acceptable.
Section 21.10   Schedule 10 C2(2) refers to CP112.
Section 22.01   C2.
(iii)   D14, Schedules 6 & 10 — Explana-
        tory Memorandum Part C Figs. 6a
        & 6b give guidance on sizes.
Section 22.08   In Scotland it is normal practice to
        provide a sarking board on top of
        the rafters and below the sarking
        felt. Traditionally this was 15 mm
        sawn softwood boarding which in a
        slated roof avoided the need for
        battens. Wood has now been partly
        replaced by materials such as
        bitumen impregnated fibreboard
        and foil-backed plasterboard, both
        requiring the use of battens for
        slates and tiles.
Section 22.15   No materials are specifically
        approved for this purpose but a
        number are given in deemed-to-
        satisfy specifications in Schedule 10:
        J3(1).
Section 22.17   Designed to CP 112 requirements.
Section 23.06   D5.
        Schedule 9, Table 3, Part VI lists
        typical constructions with their
        notional period of fire resistance.
Section 23.08   The sheet materials do not require
        to have a period of fire resistance
        if they are taken to be an opening
        as specified in D2. This may increase
        the minimum distance of the
        building from the boundary.

A checklist of books in the Newnes-Butterworths Technician Series

MATHEMATICS FOR TECHNICIANS 1

FRANK TABBERER, Chichester College of Technology

This is an introduction to mathematics for the student technician, intended especially to cover mathematics at level one in TEC courses (core unit U75/005). The presentation will create an interest in the subject particularly for those students who have previously found maths a stumbling block. There are frequent examples and exercises, with a summary and revision exercise at the end of each chapter.

CONTENTS: Manipulating numbers. Calculations. Algebra. Graphs and mappings. Statistics. Geometry. Trigonometry.

192 pages   May 1978   0 408 00326 X

MATHEMATICS FOR TECHNICIANS 2

FRANK TABBERER, Chichester College of Technology

This covers mathematics at level two in TEC courses (units U75/012 and either U75/038 or U75/039), for those who have completed (or gained exemption from) the work in *Mathematics for Technicians 1.* It includes the alternative schemes of work allowed in the second stage of level two. The clear presentation and systems of examples and exercises, similar to those in the first volume, will enable students to gain a real grasp of the subject.

CONTENTS: Trigonometry (1). Areas and volumes. Statistics (1). Graphs. Trigonometry (2). Equations and graphs. Mensuration. Statistics (2). Introduction to calculus.

156 pages   September 1978   0 408 00371 5

PHYSICAL SCIENCE FOR TECHNICIANS 1

R. McMULLAN, Willesden College of Technology

This is intended for students studying the Physical Science level one unit of programmes leading to TEC certificates and diplomas. The text meets the requirements of the standard TEC syllabus for physical science (unit U75/004), a core unit of courses in building, civil engineering, electrical engineering and mechanical engineering. Attention has been paid to the visual presentation of the text, which is illustrated with diagrams and examples. Important concepts and formulae are clearly highlighted as an aid to learning and revision.

CONTENTS: Introduction. Fundamentals. Force and materials. Structure of matter. Work, energy, power. Heat. Waves. Electricity. Force and motion. Forces at rest. Pressure and fluids. Chemical reactions. Light.

96 pages   May 1978   0 408 00332 4

ELECTRICAL PRINCIPLES FOR TECHNICIANS 2

S. A. KNIGHT, Bedford College of Higher Education

Easy to read and in close conformity with the TEC syllabus, this book is intended primarily to cover TEC unit U75/019, Electrical Principles 2, an essential unit for both telecommunications and electronics students. The text includes examples, worked out for the reader, as well as problems for self-assessment, answers to which will be found at the end of the book. SI units are used exclusively throughout.

CONTENTS: Units and definitions. Series and parallel circuits. Electrical networks. Capacitors and capacitance. Capacitors in circuit. Magnetism and magnetisation. Electromagnetic induction. Alternating voltages and currents. Magnetic circuits. Reactance and impedance. Power and resonance. A.C. to D.C. conversion. Instruments and measurements. Alternating current measurements.

144 pages   May 1978   0 408 00325 1

ELECTRONICS FOR TECHNICIANS 2

S. A. KNIGHT, Bedford College of Higher Education

Provides an introduction to the basic theory and application of semiconductors. It covers the essential syllabus and requirements of TEC unit U76/010, Electronics 2, though some additional notes have been added for clarity. The text includes examples and self-assessment problems.

CONTENTS: Thermionic and semiconductor theory. Semiconductor and thermionic diodes. Applications of semiconductor diodes. The bipolar transistor. The transistor as amplifier. Oscillators. The cathode ray tube. Logic circuits. Electronic gate elements.

112 pages   June 1978   0 408 00324 3

BUILDING TECHNOLOGY 1 & 2

JACK BOWYER, Croydon College of Arts and Technology

These textbooks are primarily intended for the building technician taking TEC B2 construction courses. The clarity of text and illustrations should also, however, appeal to students of architecture and quantity surveying who need a good solid grounding in building construction.

BUILDING TECHNOLOGY 1

CONTENTS: The building industry. Site investigation, setting out and plant. Building elements: practice and materials. The substructure of building. The superstructure of building. Appendix: Building Standards (Scotland) Regulations 1971—75.

96 pages   March 1978   0 408 00298 0

BUILDING TECHNOLOGY 2

CONTENTS: First fixing joinery and windows. Services and drainage. Finishes and finishings. Second fixing joinery and doors. Site works, roads and pavings. Appendix: Building Standards (Scotland) Regulations 1971—75.

96 pages   May 1978   0 408 00299 9

HEATING AND HOT WATER SERVICES FOR TECHNICIANS

KEITH MOSS, City of Bath Technical College

By a system of nearly 200 worked examples, the author describes the routine design procedures for heating and hot water services in commercial and industrial buildings. Primarily intended for student HVAC technicians (TEC sector B3), it will also be useful for other students in sectors B2 and B3, and as a revision aid for experienced HVAC technicians encountering a change from Imperial to SI measurement.

CONTENTS: Heat energy transfer. Heat energy requirements of heated buildings. Heat energy losses from heated buildings. Space heating appliances. Heat energy emission. Heating and hot water service systems. The feed and expansion tank. Three-way control valves and boiler plant diagrams. Steam generation. Steam systems. Preliminary pipe sizing. Circuit balancing. Hydraulic resistance in pipes and fittings. Proportioning pipe emission. Hot and cold water supply. Circulating pumps. Steam and condense pipe sizing. Heat losses using environmental temperature. Medium and high pressure hot water heating.

168 pages   July 1978   0 408 00300 6

NOTES

NOTES

NOTES

NOTES

NOTES